Christina Reid

JOYRIDERS and

DID YOU HEAR THE ONE ABOUT THE IRISHMAN?

Introduction and questions by Caroline Jeffs

Heinemann Educational Publishers
Halley Court, Jordan Hill, Oxford OX2 8EJ
a division of Reed Educational & Professional Publishing Ltd
MELBOURNE   AUCKLAND
FLORENCE   PRAGUE   MADRID   ATHENS
SINGAPORE   TOKYO   SAO PAULO
PORTSMOUTH NH   MEXICO CITY
IBADAN   GABORONE   JOHANNESBURG
KAMPALA   NAIROBI

ACKNOWLEDGEMENT
The extract from *Shadow of a Gunman* by Sean O'Casey was taken from "Sean O'Casey
– Collected Plays Vol. 1" and is reproduced by kind permission of Macmillan Ltd,
London and Basingstoke.

Joyriders first published by Methuen 1987
Did You Hear the One About the Irishman . . .? A Love Story first published by Methuen 1989
Published in the *Heinemann Plays* series 1993

06 05 04 03 02 01 00 99 98 97
13 12 11 10 9 8 7 6 5 4 3

A catalogue record for this book is available from the British Library on request.
ISBN 0 435 23292 4

DEDICATION
Fabian Cartwright, who played Tommy in the first production of *Joyriders*, died aged 28 in
1989. This edition of the play is dedicated to him with much love.

Cover design by Keith Pointing
Designed by Jeffery White Creative Associates
Typeset by Taurus Graphics, Kidlington, Oxon
Printed by Clays Ltd, St Ives plc

CONTENTS

PREFACE

In this edition of *Joyriders* and *Did You Hear the One About the Irishman . . . ?* you will find notes, questions and activities to help in studying the play in class, particularly at GCSE level.

The introduction provides background information on the author, the writing of the plays and their historical and political context.

The activities at the end of the book range from straightforward *Keeping Track* questions which can be tackled at the end of each act to focus close attention on what is happening in the play, to more detailed work on characters, themes and criticism in *Explorations*.

At the end of the book there is a glossary, arranged by acts, for easy reference.

INTRODUCTION

Christina Reid

Christina Reid was born in Belfast in 1942 into an Ulster Protestant working-class family. Her father was a docker and a gambler and her mother supported the family by working part-time as a waitress in hotels and in establishments such as the Ulster Reform Club and the Jewish Institute.

Her grandfather had been in the British Army in the First World War and her uncle died from wounds he received at Dunkirk.

At home she was taught to be 'proud to be Irish' and 'more British than the British' all at the same time. Although she was raised as a Protestant, Reid now says, 'I have no belief in churches or creeds, and fundamentalism of any sort appals me.'

'My earliest memory of writing,' she recalls, 'is in early childhood when I was given a five year diary (white leather with a lock and key) and instead of recording facts, I made it all up.'

She was surrounded during her childhood by both Irish street songs and British music-hall songs. 'My earliest memory of theatre is of my mother and the women of her family dressing up and singing and dancing as they enacted stories that were a mixture of fact, fantasy and folklore.' Reid was later to use the essence of these women and their bawdy, irreverent humour as the starting point for her play *The Belle of the Belfast City*.

She left school at fifteen. Having been taught only English history in school, Reid says that she left 'with very little knowledge of the history of my own country. I learned that mainly by reading and by questioning things I'd been brought up never to question.'

There followed a series of boring office jobs, including working for the Northern Ireland Civil Service, which she was forced to leave when she married in 1964, as at that time they did not employ married women!

Whilst raising three children, Christina Reid studied for 'O' and 'A' levels at night school, and in 1982 went to Queens University, Belfast as a mature student to read English, Sociology and Russian Studies.

Did You Hear the One About the Irishman . . . ? was her first play and was an immediate success. It won the Ulster TV Drama Award in 1980 and went on to be staged by the Royal Shakespeare Company on tour in New York and Washington in 1982.

After the death of her mother, Reid wrote *Tea in a China Cup*. It won the Thames TV Playwright Scheme Award in 1983 which made her Writer-in-Residence at the Lyric Theatre, Belfast. She abandoned her degree course to accept the post.

Joyriders was commissioned and produced in 1986 by Paines Plough, the Writers' Company, and a national tour followed.

When her marriage broke up in the 1980s Christina Reid moved permanently to London. She was Writer-in-Residence at the Young Vic Theatre in London in 1988/89.

Although she prefers writing for the stage 'because of the chance to watch a play grow by working with the actors,' Reid now does much of her work for TV and radio. Other plays have included *The Last of a Dyin' Race* in 1986 and *My Name? Shall I Tell You My Name?* in 1987.

Christina Reid's work has been described as belonging to a new vein of 'flinty documentary' (Michael Coveney, *Financial Times*) which is revitalising Northern Irish theatre. She writes about a community she knows from the inside, and whose people, traditions and loyalties she clearly understands.

Joyriders

In 1983–84 when Christina Reid was a resident writer in the Lyric Theatre, Belfast, a group of teenagers on a Youth Training Scheme came to see a production of *Shadow of a Gunman*. Most of them had never been in a theatre before, and their reactions to the play and the place made her want to write a play about them.

'They were hilarious,' she remembers. 'They ate crisps, smoked, went in and out to the toilet whenever they liked. They all cheered when Donal Davoren kissed Minnie.' When Reid met them afterwards she asked them what they had thought of the play, and it was quite clear that most of them were unimpressed or not at ease in the middle-class atmosphere of theatre.

This meeting was the inspiration for the opening scene of *Joyriders*. Reid was invited by the group to visit them at their Youth Training Scheme, which was based in a disused linen mill. She set most of the action for *Joyriders* in the same environment. She visited other YTS schemes and this led to a meeting in the Community Centre, Divis Flats (which has been described as the worst housing development in Western Europe). There she met a group of residents who had written and performed songs about their life in Belfast. These songs, stories and conversations became the basis for *Joyriders*.

The play's title refers to the teenage craze of stealing a car and driving recklessly at high speeds. In Belfast, the dangers of crashing and of being caught by the police are compounded by the threats both of the IRA, who deal out their own punishments (beatings and kneecapping) to law-breakers operating outside their control, and of the Army, who are likely to open fire on any car that races through a check-point or road-block.

In the play, Sandra says of joyriding, 'It usta be a laugh. It stopped bein' funny the day the Brits stopped shoutin' "halt" and opened fire.' But the title has a broader signi-ficance too. If a joyride is something which is fun for a while, but is ultimately pointless, then Sandra sees that that is what the YTS project is for teenagers who have no hope of getting a real job at the end of it: 'It's a friggin' government joyride. A good laugh for a year an' then ye grow up.'

Did You Hear the One About the Irishman . . . ? A Love Story

The play began as a reaction to the violence in the 1970s in Belfast. 'It took shape,' says Reid, 'because of three things in particular that filled me with horror and anger and despair. I learned of the sectarian murder of a girl I had worked with; I visited the Maze Prison Long Kesh; and I watched an English comedian reduce a television audience to hysterical laughter with racist Irish jokes.'

The first version of the play was written for television, but although the script won an award it was not produced. It was taken on tour by the RSC in America, and was finally shown in Britain when an updated version was performed at the King's Head Pub Theatre in London.

During the play, Reid juxtaposes the straight-faced Irishman reading lists of permitted gifts, items of clothing and food, which are allowed in the Maze Prison, with the familiar figure of the stand-up comedian with his endless supply of Irish jokes. What begins as a startling contrast between the two gradually works on the audience, first to draw attention to the bizarre nature of some of the forbidden items mentioned in the lists, but then to make us feel increasingly uncomfortable with the distasteful jokes. By the end of the play, when we have come to know and care about the fate of the characters, the stony face of the Irishman betrays the despair he, and we, feel, while the relentlessly jaunty comedian is painfully off-key.

There is, moreover, a distinct contrast between the self-deprecating and often black humour, with which Allison and Brian discuss their situation, and the racial stereotypes of the English comedian's jokes.

'*Did You Hear the One* . . . ? is an exploration of prejudice where no one is immune and where the jokes are no joke.' (Peggy Butcher, *Time Out*)

Historical and Political Background

The troubles which divide Catholics and Protestants in Northern Ireland today have their roots far back in history. British claims to rule on Irish land can be traced as far back as the twelfth century. For hundreds of years the English attempted to colonize Ireland, and the Irish rebelled against English landlords. In the seventeenth century, after England had become a Protestant country, but Ireland remained Catholic, thousands of English and Scottish Protestants were given grants to emigrate to Ireland. This was encouraged by James I, who saw it as a way of preventing further rebellions against English rule.

A concerted attempt to convert the Irish to Protestantism in the seventeenth century was strenuously resisted, and when James II, a Catholic, came to the British throne in 1685, this was warmly welcomed in Ireland.

However, his position was not secure. Protestants opposed to James invited Prince William of Orange and his wife, Mary, to accept the throne of England, and James II fled.

In 1690 King William defeated forces loyal to James at the Battle of the Boyne, and thus the so-called Protestant Ascendancy was confirmed in Ireland. By the end of the century, although 75% of the population were Catholics, they owned only 14% of the land.

For over two hundred years Ireland was governed by the English Parliament, though there was a constant struggle for independence. During this time Orange Lodges were formed to assert the Protestant movement, and this was countered by the Catholic Association, which promoted the cause of Irish nationalism. Political movements also sprang up: Unionists supported continuing government from London, while the Irish Republican Brotherhood campaigned for an end to British rule.

Industrial prosperity in the nineteenth century centred around Belfast. Belfast was Protestant heartland, but working class Catholics were needed to work in the factories.

By 1880 there was a major campaign for Home Rule led by Charles Stewart Parnell, who for a while succeeded in uniting many different factions in Ireland in the fight for independence. When he was forced to resign, however, the movement collapsed.

The next decades saw a terrible conflict between Protestants and Catholics, especially in Belfast, where Catholics were often driven out of jobs. Violence erupted frequently, but surprisingly the First World War saw a decline in nationalism and thousands of Irishmen fought with the British forces.

It was the actions of a small band of rebels in Dublin in 1916 which reversed this trend. They started an armed rebellion and seized the Post Office as their headquarters. They were easily overwhelmed by British troops, but the British authorities over-reacted to the revolt. The ringleaders were executed, and thousands of people were arrested and imprisoned. These actions turned many moderate Irish people into fervent nationalists, and when the war was over they were determined to have self-rule.

In the following years violence escalated – there was an increase in terrorist activity, there were sectarian riots and the Royal Irish Constabulary (among them many special constables, or Black and Tans) were renowned for their brutality.

The need to reach an agreement about Home Rule became urgent. Lloyd George began discussions with Irish leaders in 1921, and eventually a treaty was signed, but six counties in the north of Ireland, where the majority of the people were Protestant, and loyal to Britain, were excluded. Ireland was partitioned: the largest part became the Irish Free State (later Eire) and the rest Northern Ireland and part of the United Kingdom.

The Catholic minority in the North was left high and dry. Political affinities were drawn almost exclusively along religious lines. The Protestant majority found it easy to discriminate against Catholics. Eventually, in the 1960s the Catholic minority began to organise civil rights protests.

In 1967 and 1968 there were outbreaks of sectarian violence, and deaths in the 'Troubles.' As this grew more and more serious in 1969, the British army were drafted into Northern Ireland, where they remain to this day. Violence and sectarian killings continue on both sides.

Shadow of a Gunman by Sean O'Casey: a note

The play is set in Dublin in 1920, against a background of

unrest and confrontation between the local population and the Royal Irish Constabulary. The central character, Donal Davoran, is a writer living in a tenement house. When his fellow residents leap to the conclusion that he is a gunman working for the IRA, he is content to let them believe it, basking in the glamour that seems to accord him.

However, his room-mate, Seamus Shields, unwittingly looks after a bag which turns out to contain explosives.

To save his own skin when the special constables (also known as the Black and Tans) raid the house, Davoran allows Minnie, a young girl who is infatuated with him, to take the blame. She is arrested, and shot when she tries to escape.

JOYRIDERS

Setting and Background

Joyriders takes place mainly in the former Lagan Linen Mill where the Youth Training Programme now operates. There is one scene in a Belfast theatre, one in Kate's house, one in the Arts Council Gallery, Belfast.

The walls of the linen mill are decorated with the teenagers' paintings of Belfast street life and samples of the work produced on the knitting machines. There is a lot of graffiti, mainly in the form of abbreviations:

F.T.P.	FUCK THE POPE
F.T.Q.	FUCK THE QUEEN
U.T.H.	UP THE HOODS
I.R.A.	IRISH REPUBLICAN ARMY
I.N.L.A.	IRISH NATIONAL LIBERATION ARMY
U.D.A.	ULSTER DEFENCE ASSOCIATION
U.V.F.	ULSTER VOLUNTEER FORCE
L.P.W.	LOYALIST PRISONERS OF WAR
L.F.C.	LINFIELD FOOTBALL CLUB
C.F.C.	CELTIC FOOTBALL CLUB
G.F.C.	GLENTORAN FOOTBALL CLUB

There are also some slogans:

No Pope Here – No friggin' wonder
Fuck 1690. We want a re-run
The Pope is a Para – Paisley for Pope
God save Ulster/The Queen/The Pope/Us
God Love Big Sandra
Jesus saves with the Abbey National
Give us a job. What's a job?
Is there a life before death?
Snuff is high class glue.
Joyriders live. Joyriders die.

The mixture of Protestant/Catholic graffiti is due mainly to jokers, but also because there will be a small number of Protestant teenagers among the predominantly Catholic teenagers on the course.

This particular training programme is mainly peopled by young offenders on probation or suspended sentence for petty crime and joyriding.

Cast

SANDRA   Aged 16–17. Tough, cynical, intelligent. Protects herself by refusing to believe in or aspire to anything.

MAUREEN   Aged 16–17. Hopeful, dreamy. Lives alone with and constantly worried about her 12-year-old brother Johnnie who is a compulsive joyrider and glue-sniffer.

ARTHUR   Aged 17–18. A skinhead by accident rather than choice. Was accidentally shot by the army. His injuries have left him with a shaven head, a scarred face and a limp. He looks dangerous/menacing, but is in general a cheerful joker.

TOMMY   Aged 17–18. Slight physical signs of possible mixed racial parentage. Interested in politics. Steals for himself and for others.

KATE   Aged 34. A social worker in charge of the Youth Training Programme that the four teenagers are attending. Middle class, concerned, committed. Frustrated by the futility of the scheme. Tries to interest the teenagers in theatre, art, and so on.

Joyriders was commissioned and produced by Paines Plough, The Writers Company, and opened at the Tricycle Theatre on 13 February 1986, prior to a nationwide tour with the following cast.

SANDRA	Michelle Fairley
MAUREEN	Clare Cathcart
ARTHUR	Gerard O'Hare
TOMMY	Fabian Cartwright
KATE	Veronica Duffy

Voice-overs in *Shadow of a Gunman*

MRS GRIGSON	Sheila Hancock
DONAL DAVOREN	Stephen Rea
SEAMUS SHIELDS	John Thaw

Director	Pip Broughton
Designer	Ellen Cairns
Lighting Designer	Jim Simmons
Assistant Director	Jeremy Raison
Stage Managers	Margaret Sutherland
	Robin Nash
	Imogen Bertin

The songs in *Joyriders* were written and first performed by residents of Divis Flats working with Clair Chapman. For information on where to obtain musical scores, etc., apply to Alan Brodie Representation, 91 Regent Street, London W1R 7TB.

In November 1985, the Divis Residents Association and the Town and Country Planning Association, London, held an exhibition of photographs of the Divis Flats complex in Belfast, which was described as the worst housing development in Western Europe. These flats provide the background for *Joyriders.*

The action of the play takes place between February and May 1986.

Prologue

Belfast Street Song

FIRST VOICE:	Everywhere we go
SECOND VOICE:	Everywhere we go
FIRST VOICE:	People always ask us
SECOND VOICE:	People always ask us
FIRST VOICE:	Who we are
SECOND VOICE:	Who we are
FIRST VOICE:	And where do we come from
SECOND VOICE:	And where do we come from
FIRST VOICE:	And we always tell them
SECOND VOICE:	And we always tell them
FIRST VOICE:	We're from Belfast
SECOND VOICE:	We're from Belfast
FIRST VOICE:	Mighty mighty mighty mighty mighty mighty Belfast
SECOND VOICE:	Mighty mighty mighty mighty mighty mighty Belfast
FIRST VOICE:	And if they can't hear us
SECOND VOICE:	And if they can't hear us
FIRST VOICE:	We shout a little louder
SECOND VOICE:	We shout a little louder

(Repeat song louder, and an octave higher. End with:
'And if they can't hear us, they must be deaf'.)

ACT ONE

Mid-February 1986.

A theatre in Belfast. KATE, SANDRA, MAUREEN, ARTHUR *and* TOMMY *watching the end of Sean O'Casey's play 'Shadow of a Gunman'.* KATE *and* TOMMY *both watch intently.* ARTHUR *is grinning.* SANDRA *is bored.* MAUREEN *is in tears. Sound of explosion, gunfire, then voice over.*

Scene One

VOICE OVER (*Mrs Grigson*): What's goin' to happen next? Oh, Mr Davoren, isn't it terrible? Isn't it terrible? Minnie Powell, poor little Minnie Powell's been shot dead! They were raidin' a house a few doors down, an' had just got up in their lorries to go away, when they was ambushed. You never heard such shootin'. An' in the thick of it, poor Minnie went to jump off the lorry she was on, an' she was shot through the bozzum. (ARTHUR *grins at the word bozzum, nudges* SANDRA). Oh it was horrible to see the blood pourin' out, an' Minnie moanin'. They found some paper in her breast (ARTHUR *nudges* SANDRA *again*) with Minnie written on it, an' some other name they couldn't make out with the blood; the officer kep' it. The ambulance is bringin' her to the hospital, but what good's that when she's dead. Poor little Minnie, poor little Minnie Powell, to think of you full of a life a few minutes ago, an' now she's dead!

VOICE OVER (*Donal Davoren*): Ah me, alas! Pain, pain, pain ever for ever. It's terrible to think that poor little Minnie is dead, but it's still more terrible to think that Davoren and Shields are alive! Oh, Donal Davoren, shame is your portion now till the silver cord is loosened and the golden bowl be broken. Oh Davoren, Donal Davoren, poet and poltroon, poltroon and poet!

VOICE OVER (*Seamus Shields*): I knew something ud come of the tappin' on the wall.

Sounds of audience applause. KATE *and* MAUREEN
applaud. TOMMY *and* SANDRA *do not applaud.* ARTHUR
gives a slow handclap, whistles.

ARTHUR *and* SANDRA *go to get up.*

KATE   We might as well sit here until the crowd clears.

TOMMY   What for? Are we not good enough to mingle with
the fur-coat brigade in the foyer?

ARTHUR   You know what they say Sandra? Fur coat, no
knickers.

SANDRA *takes out a cigarette.*

KATE   Sandra, I've already told you, no smoking in the
auditorium.

ARTHUR   Are you allowed to pee in the auditorium? Only, I
need to go now.

KATE   Arthur, you went four times during the play. You
couldn't need to go again.

ARTHUR   I've got a damaged bladder.

KATE   No you haven't. You were injured in the head and
legs. All the parts in between are in perfect working
order.

ARTHUR   (*leering at* SANDRA): That's true.

SANDRA   Piss off Arthur.

ARTHUR   Are you all right Maureen?

MAUREEN You're rotten. Laughin' when the girl got shot.

ARTHUR   How could you feel sorry for a girl called Minnie?

SANDRA   She was pathetic. Gettin' killed to save him.

MAUREEN She was brave. It was lovely.

TOMMY   It wasn't lovely. (*He speaks slowly as if quoting from
a political text book.*) It was a comment on what
happens to people what are kep' down by the yoke
of British imperialism.

ARTHUR   Is that what it was? I thought he just wanted to
screw her, but he hadn't the nerve.

SANDRA   All talk, like you Arthur.

ARTHUR   Come roun' the back an' talk to me then.

MAUREEN   Minnie loved him, that's why she died for him.

SANDRA   He wouldn't die for her though, would he? Some hero. All mouth, no action.

KATE   That's why O'Casey called him the Shadow of a Gunman.

ARTHUR   He was a five-star wanker.

MAUREEN   He was a poet.

SANDRA   He was a shite.

TOMMY   He was a nuthin'. People like him what sit on the political fence live on while the innocent die.

SANDRA   Tommy, you must be the most borin' person on God's earth.

ARTHUR   He's the one what's all talk, like him in the play . . . whadyecallhim . . .

KATE   Davoren, Donal Davoren.

TOMMY   Whadye mean?

ARTHUR   All his big ideas come from books. So do yours.

TOMMY   I don't just read about it. I know a few of the lads.

SANDRA   We all know a few of the lads. They live in the same rotten housin' on the same rotten road we do.

TOMMY   I've done them a few small favours.

ARTHUR   Like what?

TOMMY   Nothin' I can talk about.

ARTHUR   Because you've got nuthin' to talk about, that's why. Yer all mouth.

MAUREEN   Donal really loved Minnie.

SANDRA   Aye, enough to let her die. You're as soft as she was. Kate, can we go now, I'm dying' fer a feg.

ARTHUR   An' my willie's bustin'.

SANDRA   Arthur, do you never think of nuthin' else? You think you're God's gift.

ARTHUR   When I get my compensation fer the accident, you'll all be after my body.

SANDRA   Arthur, I wouldn't have ye if ye were studded with diamonds.

ARTHUR   You'd have me, wouldn't ye Maureen?

SANDRA   Maureen's in love with Nik Kershaw.

MAUREEN   I like his records.

SANDRA   (*sings mockingly*): Wouldn't it be good to be in your shoes, even if it was for just one day . . .

TOMMY,
SANDRA,   (*sing*): Wouldn't it be good if we could wish
ARTHUR   our cares away . . .

KATE   Well, as the philosophical discussion on the play appears to be over, I'll go and get the car. You wait here. It's still raining. No point in us all getting soaked. I'll see you in the foyer in about five minutes.

ARTHUR   You givin' us all a lift home, Kate?

KATE   Right to your front doors. That way you'll get to bed early and be in on time in the morning.

SANDRA   Any word of me gettin' off them stupid knittin' machines and onto car maintenance?

KATE   I've already had a word with the project leader. I've to see him again at the end of the week.

SANDRA   He doesn't want me there, does he?

KATE   He thinks you wouldn't be strong enough to handle a lot of the work.

SANDRA   I'm bigger than half them wee lads doin' it.

ARTHUR   Weemin don't repair cars.

SANDRA   If you can do caterin' I can change a sparkin' plug.

ARTHUR   All the greatest chefs is men.

SANDRA   Aye, because women get landed with the cookin' jobs that pay buttons, or nuthin' at all.

KATE   I'll get the car.

           She exits.

MAUREEN	It must be lovely to have yer own car. Drive out till the country an' all.
SANDRA	Get your Johnnie to steal one for ye.
MAUREEN	Johnnie doesn't do that no more.
SANDRA	You mean he hasn't got caught for a while.
MAUREEN	He's stopped. He's working hard at school.
SANDRA	Tell that to the probation officer.
ARTHUR	Maybe I'll buy a car out of my compensation.
TOMMY	You haven't a hope in hell of gettin' compensation.
ARTHUR	My solicitor says we have a good case.
TOMMY	The British Army have the best case goin'. The courts is on their side. No judge here is gonna convict a soldier of attempted murder.
ARTHUR	It's not that sort of case. Nobody's on trial. Nobody has to get convicted of nuthin'. All my solicitor has to prove is that the Brits opened fire on a joyrider an' I got hit by accident. He has to prove that I wasn't doin' nuthin'.
TOMMY	Maureen's ma wasn't doin' nuthin'. She didn't get no compensation.
	A small silence at the mention of MAUREEN'S *mother.*
SANDRA	Shut up Tommy. Come on Maureen and we'll have a smoke.
MAUREEN	I haven't got no fegs.
SANDRA	We'll share one.
	The girls exit.
ARTHUR	We'll all go to the bar, share a pint before Kate gets back.
TOMMY	They won't serve us.
ARTHUR	They won't know we're under age.
TOMMY	I don't mean that. Did you see the way they looked at us when we come in? This is a middle-class theatre. Not for the likes of us.

ARTHUR	My money's as good as anybody else's.
TOMMY	How much have ye got left out of Maggie Thatcher's twenty-seven poun' thirty pence?
ARTHUR	Enough to buy a pint.
TOMMY	I bet ye a poun' they won't serve ye.
ARTHUR	Yer on. Here, if they don't serve us, how'll we know why?
TOMMY	By the way they look at ye.
SONG:	'Children of Divis Flats'

We are the children of Divis Flats
And it's for houses that we're fighting   Repeat
A place to live a place to play
A place for health and happiness   Repeat
They took our houses they gave us flats
How much longer must we live here?   Repeat
We are the children of Divis Flats
And it's for houses that we're fighting   Repeat
Among the rats, among the clocks
And breathing in asbestos   Repeat
We are the children of Divis Flats
And it's for houses that we're fighting   Repeat

Scene Two

The Lagan Mill. The following morning. TOMMY
*comes in, looks around to make sure no one is
about. Lifts a catering bag of tea bags, tosses it to
someone offstage. Lifts a catering tin of coffee, tosses
it to someone offstage. Goes to a clock card machine.
Clocks in. Exits.* MAUREEN *enters, clocks in, goes and
sits down at a knitting machine. Looks at her watch,
goes to* KATE'*s phone, dials.*

MAUREEN	Hello, is that you, Mr McAuley. It's Maureen Reilly. Our Johnnie's not well, he won't be into school the day . . . what? . . . he's got . . . a cold . . . and a sore throat . . . he'll be in the morra . . . no he's not mitchin', he's not well, so he's not.

KATE *comes in, overhears part of the conversation.*

MAUREEN	Sorry Kate, I would've asked, but ye weren't about.
KATE	It's all right.
MAUREEN	I'll see ye later.
KATE	Maureen?
MAUREEN	What?
KATE	Sit down a minute.
MAUREEN	I've a lot on the day.
KATE	What's the matter with Johnnie?
MAUREEN	He's not well.
KATE	What way not well? (*Pause.*) Has he been on the glue again?
MAUREEN	No . . . I don't know . . . he was in bed when I got home last night. About six o'clock this mornin' I heard him vomitin'. He was as sick as a dog.
KATE	Where is he now?
MAUREEN	In the house. He's all right, just a bit green aroun' the gills. He'll sleep it off. He got fish an' chips in Larry's last night. I'm always tellin' him not to eat anything out of that dirty hole. The health man shoulda closed that dive down years ago. I don't know how that oul Larry gets away with it.
KATE	When does Johnnie see his probation officer again?
MAUREEN	Friday.
KATE	I think you should give her a call today.
MAUREEN	No.
KATE	Maureen, Claudia's job is to help Johnnie and you. She's on your side.
MAUREEN	She works for them, and they wanta put Johnnie away.
KATE	Her job is to prevent that happening.
MAUREEN	You shoulda seen the oul magistrate, old as the hills kep' sayin' to me 'Speak up, girl, I can't hear you.' As if it was my fault he was half deaf. He told our

Johnnie if he got caught doin' anything again he'd
put him away an' no more chances.

KATE   He would have been put in a home if Claudia hadn't
convinced the magistrate that you were capable and
reliable and fit to look after him. She made promises
on your behalf, Maureen. Don't let her down. You
have got to let her know if Johnnie's on the glue
again.

MAUREEN   He's not. It was Larry's oul re-heated fish.

KATE   If he's sniffing again, he'll be out joyriding before
the week's out.

MAUREEN   I told you. He's not sniffin' nuthin'. That Larry has a
lot to answer for.

KATE   Claudia will have a lot to answer for if Johnnie gets
himself injured, or injures somebody else.

MAUREEN   You're not worried about our Johnnie nor me.
You're just afraid yer chum Claudia'll get intil
trouble for not doin' her job right.

KATE   I'm afraid that Johnnie might get shot.

MAUREEN   Don't say that.

KATE   Not saying it doesn't mean it's not happening.

MAUREEN   The ones what got shot were big lads. Our Johnnie's
only twelve.

*TOMMY has come in and overhead part of the
conversation.*

TOMMY   I never heard of the security forces checkin' anybody's
age, name and address before they opened fire.

*MAUREEN walks out. She passes ARTHUR who is clocking
in.*

ARTHUR   Mornin' sweetheart.

MAUREEN   Away an' jump.

ARTHUR   What did I say?

*He puts on a white coat and a chef's hat. Gets things
ready for the morning tea break. Sets out cups, fills
the tea urn with water, etc.*

KATE	Okay, Tommy. Where's the paint?
TOMMY	What paint?
KATE	Two litres of white gloss, two litres of varnish, and a plastic container of white spirit.
TOMMY	I'm only in. Ask themens in the joinery section.
KATE	I was here very early, long before any of you got in. Stocktaking. The stuff has already gone.
TOMMY	Some bugger broke in durin' the night?
KATE	Stop acting the innocent. It went missing yesterday when you were in charge of the sixteen-year-olds who were painting the lockers.
TOMMY	The wee buggers. Wait'll I get the houl of them.
KATE	Has it already been sold?
TOMMY	How would I know?
KATE	Is this one for yourself or are you doing another wee homer? Redecorating some poor old pensioner's flat?
TOMMY	It would take more than a licka paint to make any of them flats fit to live in.
KATE	I want it back, Tommy, and I want it back today.
TOMMY	What's a couple of friggin' tins of paint til the government?
KATE	When you nick paint from here, you're not stealing from the government, you're stealing from your own people.
TOMMY	You can't steal from people who own nuthin'.
KATE	Yes you can Tommy. You can steal away the only chance they have.
TOMMY	Of what! Of workin' fer slave wages? . . . Why are we not allowed to make a profit on what we do here?
KATE	We must not come into competition with local industry.

TOMMY   What local industry? What you mean is, it would be really embarrassing if this underfunded project made a profit. People might start askin' if we can do it, why couldn't John de Lorean.

KATE   Tommy, this project is not about profit . . .

TOMMY   No, it's about keepin' the unemployment figures down and keepin' the likes of us off the streets.

KATE   It also keeps you out of borstal.

TOMMY   An' that's the only reason I'm here. Me an' all the other ones on probation or suspended sentence. Like they said, ye can go on the scheme or get locked up.

KATE   So why don't you help to make it work?

TOMMY   I never promised to enjoy it.

KATE   Tommy, there are a lot of people who would be delighted if this place closed, who never wanted it opened in the first place. They think teenagers like you should be horsewhipped and dropped into a bottomless pit, not trained to do something with all that energy . . .

TOMMY   Trained! Fer what! At the end of the friggin' year, we'll be back on the friggin' street with no friggin' jobs.

KATE   If I fiddle the books anymore, I'll have no job either. I have a year to prove that we can employ young offenders here for a tenth of what it costs to lock them away in approved institutions. If, at the end of the year, we are running at a loss and it can be proved that any of that loss was due to thieving, we've had it. The opposition will rub their sweaty hands with glee and say 'We told you so' and this place will close. (*Pause.*) Do you want to be responsible for proving that all their prejudices are right? (*Pause.*) I want that paint back, Tommy.

TOMMY   I'll have a word. See what I can do . . .

KATE   You want to do something. Try putting your Robin

Hood ideas to good use in here. Stop fighting me
. . . please . . . I need all the help I can get. (*Pause.*)

TOMMY   I won't hinder ye . . . but I won't help ye
neither.

KATE   Well, will you at least help the younger kids who
do want to be here?

TOMMY   Nobody wants to be here.

KATE   That's not true. Not everyone on this project came
through the courts. Twenty per cent chose to come.

TOMMY   Only because they get eight quid more here than
they would on the dole.

KATE   It's not just that. There's a real enthusiasm among a
lot of them, even the ones who did come through
the courts. They want to make a go of it. They want
it to work. For the first time in their lives they have
teachers who are genuinely interested in them and
what happens to them . . .

TOMMY   For what we are about to receive may the
government make us truly thankful.

KATE   I don't want your gratitude. I want you to stop
wrecking this scheme until there's something better
to take its place.

ARTHUR *comes in.*

ARTHUR   Hey Kate, there's no tea nor coffee in the kitchen.

TOMMY   Not now Arthur.

KATE   There had better be tea, coffee, sugar and a lot
more besides in that kitchen or none of you are
going to eat or drink all week. I am not buying as
much as an extra pint of milk! Is that clear?

She walks out.

ARTHUR   What did I say? What's the matter with everybody
the day? I thought it was goin' to be a good day,
you know? I woke up this mornin' and the oul leg
wasn't as bad as it sometimes is. I was able til get
outa bed myself without havin' to get my ma to do
her big Goliath crane act. I think the oul leg's

getting better. My da says if I stop limpin' before the court case, he'll kill me.

TOMMY The tea an' coffee's in one of the lockers in the joinery section. Ask wee Oliver, he'll show you where it is.

ARTHUR Listen you, you wanna thieve, you do it in your own section. I take a pride in my kitchen so I do.

TOMMY What's on the menu the day?

ARTHUR Ragout. (*He pronounces the 'T'.*)

TOMMY What?

ARTHUR French for stew.

TOMMY For Jesus sake, Arthur, nobody here wants anything that doesn't have chips with it.

ARTHUR I'm doin' chips as well. And pommes-de-terres. (*He pronounces both 'S's'.*)

TOMMY What time's yer break?

ARTHUR Two to three. Why?

TOMMY What are you doin' then?

ARTHUR Eatin' the leftovers.

TOMMY What else are ye doin'?

ARTHUR Chattin' up big Sandra.

TOMMY Will you give me a hand to do somethin'?

ARTHUR What?

TOMMY I need some money quick. Is that oul deaf guy still operatin' the petrol pump at the garage?

ARTHUR Ferget it. My case is comin' up. I'm not blowin' that fer a couple of quid out of a cash register.

TOMMY What'll ye do if ye get the money?

ARTHUR Make big Sandra an offer she can't refuse.

TOMMY Don't you have no ambitions?

ARTHUR Aye, to die of old age.

TOMMY I mean like helpin' other people.

ARTHUR What for? Nobody ever helped me.

TOMMY Come on, I'll get ye the tea an' coffee.

As they exit they bump into SANDRA *as she rushes in.*

ARTHUR   Mornin' darlin'.

SANDRA   Piss off.

ARTHUR   (*to* TOMMY): It must be the time of the month or somethin'.

TOMMY *and* ARTHUR *exit.*

SANDRA *punches her card. Looks at it.*

SANDRA   Shite!

She goes to MAUREEN *in the knitting machine section.*

SANDRA   One minute past. That's another fifteen-p off my wages.

MAUREEN   It's ten past.

SANDRA   I'll hafta nick a new watch, this one's hopeless. What's up with you?

MAUREEN   Nuthin'.

SANDRA   You still mopin' about that stupid play?

MAUREEN   It wasn't stupid.

SANDRA   What does it matter why people get shot? If you get shot you get shot and that's all there is to it. (MAUREEN *looks away.*) Is your ma worse, is that what's the matter?

MAUREEN   It's our Johnny. I think he's on the glue again.

SANDRA   He was never off it.

MAUREEN   He was.

SANDRA   He's a no-hoper. He always has been.

MAUREEN   I won't let them take him away.

SANDRA   You'd be better off without him.

MAUREEN   He's all I've got.

SANDRA   He's your brother. The way you talk you'd think he was your son.

MAUREEN   He's nobody's son. My da's God knows where, and my mother . . . She might as well be dead for all she knows.

SANDRA	Are ye goin' up to see her the night?
MAUREEN	I might.
SANDRA	I'll come with ye if ye like.
MAUREEN	What for?
SANDRA	I've nuthin' better to do.
MAUREEN	There's not much to do there. She just sits, starin', sayin' nuthin'.
SANDRA	Does she never speak?
MAUREEN	Every nigh an' again she opens her mouth as if she's gonna say somethin' an' then she screams. It's awful. They give her an injection an' she sleeps an' when she wakes up she just stares again.
SANDRA	Fuckin' Brits.
MAUREEN	It's not as if she got hurt bad, not like some of them . . . Have you ever seen a plastic bullet?
SANDRA	Loads of them. Every time there's a riot our kid collects them. He's small and he's fast. Dives in an' out between the legs of the Brits and the rioters. He's magic to watch.
MAUREEN	What for?
SANDRA	He sells them.
MAUREEN	Who to?
SANDRA	Tourists. Americans mostly, and some of them people what come here and write about us. A pound a bullet he gets. It's better than a paper round. He'll go far our kid. He'll have his own business when the rest of us is still on the dole.
MAUREEN	It's better here than bein' on the dole.
SANDRA	What's better about it, except that you get more money?
MAUREEN	You've got somewhere to go. Somethin' to do.
SANDRA	Like knittin' stupid sweaters that nobody wants.
MAUREEN	I have orders for five more.
SANDRA	Only because they're dirt cheap. I told Kate we'd get more down the market for them than selling them roun' here.

MAUREEN	We're not allowed. Kate has to keep to the rules. If she doesn't, they'll close the place down.
SANDRA	I don't know why they opened it in the first place. It's a waste of time.
MAUREEN	It's better than hangin' roun' the house all day.
SANDRA	My granny worked in here. It used to be a linen mill ye know.
MAUREEN	I know. My granny worked here too.
SANDRA	Did she ever tell ye about what it was like?
MAUREEN	She died young. I don't remember.
SANDRA	My granny was one of the lucky ones. Lived long enough to draw the pension. Most of her mates coughed their lungs up or died of lead poisonin' before they were forty. An' they got paid even less than we do.
MAUREEN	It's not that bad nowadays.
SANDRA	No, now ye get to die of cancer or boredom, if the army or the police don't get ye first.

She takes a screwdriver out of her pocket, unscrews part of the knitting machine.

MAUREEN	What are ye doin'?
SANDRA	I'm not doin' this no more. If the machine's broke they'll hafta put me on the cars. Friggin' Lady Summerville.
MAUREEN	Who?
SANDRA	Lady Summerville. She donated the machines. Were you not here the day she come on the visit? The week before Christmas it was.
MAUREEN	I had the flu.
SANDRA	She brought us a turkey. Arthur stuffed it with chestnuts. Friggin' chestnuts! It was diabolical. Anyway, the Lady Summerville give us a wee pep talk about how wonderful we all were, and how she give us the machines because when she was young there was a sewing room in her big house

an' the girls from the village come in and made
garments for the poor. Life's a geg isn't it?

MAUREEN   Maybe if we asked her, she's give us a machine
when our year's up here. We could go into business
on our own.

SANDRA   Maureen, grow up. Nobody is never gonna give us
nuthin'.

SONG   What will it be when we leave school
Will it be ace schemes or Y.T.P.
Will it be useful, will it be paid
We'll have to wait and see.

Hope it's work, real work
We hope it's work, real work
We hope it's work, real work
And not the dole.

Scene Three

KATE *sorting out papers on her desk. She lifts a small
dictaphone, speaks into it.*

KATE   Molly, I have a meeting this morning with the fund-
raising committee, so will you go ahead and type
out these progress reports and I'll sign them when I
get back. Also, will you type a reply to this letter
from Councillor Margaret Anderson. As you will see,
she is requesting, among other things, a breakdown
on the Catholic/Protestant ratio of teenagers in each
of the sections here. Now what is that bigoted old
bat up to now I wonder . . . Give here all the
necessary detail . . . we started out with sixty
participants and are now down to fifty . . . three
have been arrested and the other seven, all
Protestants, have been transferred to other schemes
at their own request. Make sure she understands
there was no intimidation here . . . maybe that's
what she's angling for . . . they all left because
they were understandably nervous about working in
this area . . . oh, and do point out (politely of

course) that I did warn the powers that be, this
would be a problem when we were offered these
premises, not a stone's throw away from I.R.A.
territory . . . However, there are still six cheeky,
cheerful, undaunted Protestants in the car
maintenance section, and I'm confident they'll stay
and complete the course, because they're very keen
to participate in the stock-car races we're planning
to organise in the summer . . . God and the fund-
raising committee willing . . . maybe her husband
would like to sponsor us . . . maybe he'd like to
offer all the kids here jobs in his factory . . . Tell
our beloved councillor there are fifty kids here and
we'll be lucky if we can find jobs for five of them at
the end of the year, regardless of what religion they
are . . . they friggin' know it, we friggin' know it,
and she friggin' knows it . . .

She stops as ARTHUR *comes in with a cup of tea, is
embarrassed that he has heard her swearing.*

ARTHUR (*grinning*): Cuppa tea, Kate?

KATE Tea turned up, did it?

ARTHUR And the coffee. Some dope-head shifted it til
another cupboard . . . by mistake.

KATE Arthur?

ARTHUR What?

KATE The old woman who lives next door with all those
stray cats. When you give her a free dinner, make
sure you get the plates back. We're running low.

ARTHUR You don't miss much do ye Kate.

KATE I assume it's leftovers, that you're not making her
special meals or giving her free cartons of milk. We
can't afford that.

ARTHUR Here's yer tea.

KATE Thanks . . . Arthur, if you get this compensation
money, will you leave here?

ARTHUR I'll be eighteen soon. I'll hafta leave then anyway.

KATE   No, you can stay on until the end of the year. (*Pause.*) You're a good cook, a natural.

ARTHUR   It's dead easy. You know them big restaurants must make a fortune. It's as cheap, cheaper, even to make that sort of food fresh than buy it freezed or in a tin, but they get away with chargin' double for it.

KATE   If I could arrange it, would you be interested in coming back next year to teach the new intake about cooking, catering, all that?

ARTHUR   I don't have no exams nor nuthin'.

KATE   Would you be interested?

ARTHUR   I dunno. Would I get paid?

KATE   Yes. Not a lot, but more than twenty-seven pounds and thirty pence.

ARTHUR   Money fer oul jam. They'd never wear it.

KATE   They might.

ARTHUR   Why do ye bother, Kate?

KATE   Because I'm an incurable optimist. I still have a romantic belief that if an idea is good and right, then it's possible. You're a bit of an optimist yourself, Arthur.

ARTHUR   I'm not awful sure what an optimist is . . .

KATE   It's someone who believes that . . . things will turn out all right in the end . . . or at least that it's possible to make things turn out all right.

ARTHUR   Like, if ye wanta be a cook, ye can be a cook?

KATE   Yes.

ARTHUR   They make fun of me round here, ye know. Men don't cook in West Belfast. I don't care. What's so great about bein' a casual labourer on a buildin' site? Ye get soaked to the skin an' wore out before yer time. But you see kitchens? They're magic. Bein' the youngest, I was always home from school first. Mondays in the winter was the best. My ma always did two things on a Monday, she did the weekend

washin' and she made a big pot of vegetable broth.
The kitchen walls would be streamin' with the
steam from the washin' and the soup, an' I'd come
in freezin' an' my ma would light the gas oven an'
I'd take off the wet shoes an' socks an' put my feet
in the oven an' sit drinkin' a cup of the soup . . .
soapsuds an' vegetables . . . it sounds revoltin' but
it was great . . .

(*He becomes self-conscious about what he is saying.*)

You don't know what I'm bletherin' on about, do
ye?

KATE   Smells.

ARTHUR   What?

KATE   Smells . . . my mother smells of lavender water
and silk. Expensive but discreet, and in terribly
good taste . . . Did your mother really let you
warm your feet in the oven?

ARTHUR   We don't have no central heatin'.

KATE   (*laughing wryly at herself*): I will get you a job
here, Arthur, if only to stop me getting romantic
notions about things which are purely practical . . .
and now you don't know what I'm blethering on
about, do you?

ARTHUR   I know yer sorta puttin' yerself down. Yer always
doin' that. You shouldn't. Yer too good fer in here.

KATE   What's a nice girl like me doing in a place like this?

ARTHUR   What?

KATE   It's a saying . . . from the Hollywood movies . . .
you've never heard it.

ARTHUR   No.

KATE   I keep forgetting you're all a generation beyond me.

ARTHUR   Yer not that much older than us.

KATE   I'm thirty-four, Arthur.

ARTHUR   Ye don't look it.

KATE   I feel it, and more.

ARTHUR	Why'd you never get married, Kate? Are all the fellas roun' you way deaf, dumb and blind or what? . . . Sorry, I'm speakin' outa turn . . .
KATE	It's not that I've never been asked, Arthur, it's just that . . . I'm not sure what I want . . . or who I want . . .
ARTHUR	My sister Mary's like you, over thirty an' not married an' in no hurry either. My da goes spare about it. 'There's niver been no oul maids in our family' he keeps tellin' her, as if she's stayin' single just to annoy him, like . . . sorry . . . I don't mean I think you're an oul maid, Kate . . . it's just the way my da talks . . . my da's stupid . . . our Mary says if she can't have Clint Eastwood she doesn't want nobody . . . If you could have anybody ye wanted, who would it be?
KATE	Donald Sutherland.
ARTHUR	Who?
KATE	Donald Sutherland. He's a very famous actor. One of my favourite films is the one he made with Julie Christie. 'Don't Look Now' it was called.
ARTHUR	Never seen it.
KATE	I've seen it three times. Once in the cinema. Twice on television.
ARTHUR	What's it about?
KATE	Love . . . and death . . . there's a scene in it where they make love in an apartment in Venice . . . it's unbelievably beautiful . . . tender . . . erotic . . . perfect . . . everything we all want.
ARTHUR	Hung like a horse is he?
KATE	What?
ARTHUR	Dead good-lookin' is he?
KATE	I think so . . . (*Then realising that* ARTHUR *is obliquely referring to his scarred appearance.*) But a lot of people don't find him attractive at all . . . beauty is in the eye of the beholder . . .

ARTHUR   So my ma keeps tellin' me . . . See ye later . . .
He exits.

KATE   My mother keeps telling me I'm not getting any
younger, and if I don't make a decision soon about
Roger Elliott M.D. he's going to find himself
someone else . . . someone younger who will
devote herself to providing the home and family he
says he wants . . . she never asks what I want. She
just hopes that this job is some sort of aberration I'll
grow out of before my child-bearing years are over
. . . (*She lifts the dictaphone.*) Dear Mother, I know
I'm running out of time . . . nobody knows that
more than me . . . more and more, I find myself
looking at babies in prams, knowing I don't want to
waken up some day to the realisation that I've left it
too late. Men can have babies till the day they die,
but not women. It's not fair . . . I want a baby and
I don't want to get married and I don't have the
courage to have a child alone. (*She sets the machine
down.*) There's never been no oul maids in my
family, Arthur . . . nor no unmarried mothers
either . . . and the only man who ever touched me
the way Donald Sutherland touched Julie Christie
was committed to violence, and I sent him away.
She lifts the tape again, wipes her words away.
In the hairdressing section, SANDRA *is cutting* TOMMY*'s
hair.*

SANDRA   You know somethin' Tommy, your hair's a brilliant
colour. Sorta blue-black like Superman's.

TOMMY   (*pleased*): Do you think so?

SANDRA   Aye . . . pity ye haven't got the body to go along
with the hair.

TOMMY   All-American white . . .

SANDRA   I was talkin' about muscles, not colour. You're too
touchy you, do ye know that? What's wrong with
your da bein' an Indian? My da's a cowboy, an' it
doesn't bother me.

TOMMY	He wasn't an Indian.
SANDRA	Well what was he then?
TOMMY	I dunno . . . my mother doesn't talk about it . . . she doesn't need to, everybody round here does enough talkin' for her.
SANDRA	Tommy, people round here don't talk about you because you *might* be a half-caste, they talk about you because you're *definitely* an eejit. Ye go on all the time as if ye'd swallowed a dictionary or somethin'.
TOMMY	A prophet without honour . . .
SANDRA	What?
TOMMY	Karl Marx had to leave the country of his birth.
SANDRA	Was he your da?
TOMMY	You take nuthin' serious.
SANDRA	I take a lotta things serious, but you're not one of them.
TOMMY	You're as bad as the rest of them round here. You make jokes when somebody tries to tell you the history of your own country.
SANDRA	I got enough of that at school.
TOMMY	I don't mean the great religious political con. I mean the true history of the division of the workin' classes by the owners, the capitalists.
SANDRA	Listen you. Every mornin' I get outa bed an' I look outa the window an' the soldiers is still there. That's all the history I need to know.
TOMMY	You need to know why they're there.
SANDRA	I don't, Tommy. I just want them to go away.
TOMMY	My mother says it's all God's will an' it'll pass. She believes everything's God's will, includin' me. It's how she copes.
SANDRA	Maybe yer da was an angel, Tommy. Maybe you were one of them virgin births . . . there's about one a year on this road . . . God knows how many there are in the whole of Ireland.

TOMMY	Angels are fair-skinned and blue-eyed.
SANDRA	Says who?
TOMMY	Have you ever seen a small brown angel with blue-black hair in a stained-glass window?
SANDRA	You don't believe in all that Tommy. You're a communist. It shouldn't bother ye.
TOMMY	It doesn't bother me.

SANDRA *makes a disbelieving face behind* TOMMY's *head.* ARTHUR *comes in.*

SANDRA	Hey, Arthur, you want yer head shaved?
ARTHUR	You off the knitting machines?
SANDRA	Mine's broke. I'm fillin' in the time till they let me work on the cars.
ARTHUR	You should stick to the hairdressin' Sandra, yer dead good at it.
SANDRA	Waste of time. They can't teach me nuthin' here I don't know already. I've always done everybody's hair in our house.
ARTHUR	When my hair grows will ye streak it for me?
SANDRA	Your hair's never gonna grow. Hair doesn't sprout through a steel plate.
TOMMY	It'll grow roun' it. Like one of them climbin' plants. You can put a wee trellis on yer head Arthur an' train it, like an ivy.
ARTHUR	The surgeon says it'll take a year or two. I don't want it to grow yet anway. I hafta go intil the court scarred limpin' an' bald to get the big compensation.
SANDRA	It'll never grow.
ARTHUR	I'm a skinhead, I don't care.
SANDRA	You're a chancer. Skinheads shave their hair off on purpose. Yours got shot off by the army.
TOMMY	Did you know that the white men were the first to take scalps off the Indians? The Indians only copied what they done first. I read it in a magazine.

SANDRA	It's knowin' things like that gets ye a job.
TOMMY	I'm only sayin'.
SANDRA	Will ye sit still or ye'll end up scalped.
ARTHUR	I don't remember gettin' hit. I was walkin' down the street an' all of a sudden there was all this gunfire. A wee lad about that high run past me, an' I thought, you wee bugger you nearly got me shot. An' then I looked down an' there was all this blood, an' I thought, Christ, some poor bugger *has* got shot. An' I looked aroun' an' there was nobody there but me. An' then I fainted. There was no pain nor nuthin'. That come after.
TOMMY	If that had happened anywhere else in the British Isles you woulda died. Lucky fer you it happened here.
SANDRA	Will you sit still.
TOMMY	There are surgeons here what are the best in the world at puttin' broken bodies together. I read it in a magazine.
SANDRA	They get a lotta practice here, thanks til the terrorists.
TOMMY	An' the army an' the police. (*As if he's quoting from a text book.*) Terrorists only exist because of corrupt governments.
SANDRA	Listen dick-head, if somebody gets blowed to bits, what does it matter who done it, or why they done it?
ARTHUR	It matters if yer lookin' compensation.
TOMMY	If ye never ask why, yer never gonna change nuthin'.
SANDRA	I'm forever askin' why I'm stuck in this hole. Askin' changes nuthin'.
ARTHUR	When I get my compensation I could change yer life for yer Sandra.
SANDRA	Don't hold yer breath.
	She walks off.
ARTHUR	She really fancies me, you know. It's only a matter of time.

TOMMY   Wee Oliver says you fancy Kate.

ARTHUR   Wee Oliver's head is fulla white mice.

TOMMY   You've no chance there, Arthur. Kate's doin' a line with a rich doctor up in the City Hospital, drives a big flash Volvo, so he does.

ARTHUR   How would you know?

TOMMY   Friend of mine, works there.

ARTHUR   Oh aye, brain surgeon is he?

TOMMY   No, he's one of the real workers. Cleans up the blood and guts after Kate's fancyman has finished cuttin' up the dead bodies.

ARTHUR   (*grabbing hold of* TOMMY): Take that back!

TOMMY   It's true. He does the post mortems.

ARTHUR   He's not her fancyman. She's no tart.

TOMMY   They've been knockin' round together fer years, and he's doin' a line on the quiet with one of the nurses as well.

ARTHUR   You're a lyin' hound.

TOMMY   They're puttin' bets on in the hospital about how long he can keep the two of them goin' without Kate findin' out . . . maybe we should do her a favour an' tell her . . .

ARTHUR   I'm warnin' you. You say one word of that lyin' gossip to Kate an' *you'll* end up on a slab in the City Hospital.

TOMMY   All right! All right! Keep yer hair on.

ARTHUR   Ye made it all up, didn't ye? Didn't ye?

TOMMY   I'm away to get some fegs . . . (*He moves off.*) Are ye comin'?

ARTHUR   Some of us have work to do.

TOMMY *exits.* ARTHUR *goes to* KATE's *desk where she is sitting writing. As he approaches, she sets down the* pen and sighs.

ARTHUR   You all right, Kate?

KATE   I'm bored, Arthur. Bored out of my mind writing reports, filling in forms and trying to make sense of official letters. I seem to spend more and more time sitting in here, and less and less out there with you lot.

ARTHUR   You spend a lot of time with us.

KATE   Not enough.

ARTHUR   My sister was on a trainin' scheme for six months an' she says she only clapped eyes on the man what run it once. An' even then somebody had to tell her he was the boss.

KATE   The boss . . . is that how you all see me?

ARTHUR   Well . . . that's what ye are.

KATE   What do they really think of me, Arthur? The kids out there? Sorry, I shouldn't ask you a question like that.

ARTHUR   They think yer dead-on.

KATE   But they're never completely at ease with me, are they? They don't chat to me the way they do with their section heads, the people who actually teach them how to repair cars and make things.

ARTHUR   Ach, that's because they know all themens. They're from roun' here, same as us.

KATE   And I'm not the same as you, am I? I don't speak the same language.

ARTHUR   You speak dead nice. You wouldn't wanta be like one of them pain-in-the-arse social workers what put the Belfast accent on, would ye? Ye can spot them a mile off. All training shoes an' black leather jackets. They think rollin' their own fegs and wearing' dirty jeans makes them one of the people. They're a joke. Nobody takes them serious. You're all right Kate. You don't try to be what yer not.

KATE   You know what I am Arthur? I'm a bored middle-class female who got excited by the civil rights movement in the sixties, and was so terrified by the violence that erupted around us when we marched from Belfast to Derry in the name of equal opportunities for all that I stopped marching, stopped protesting, and kidded myself that by getting a degree in social studies I could change the system from within. And here I am, fifteen years later, one of the bosses.

ARTHUR   We could do with more bosses like you.

KATE   When I was your age, Arthur, I believed there shouldn't be any bosses.

ARTHUR   That's oul commie talk. That's fer people like Tommy. Not fer people like you, Kate.

KATE   You know what I am, Arthur? A shadow of a socialist. The only difference between me and Donal Davoren is that I'm bluffing nobody but myself.

Offstage the teenagers chant.

(ARTHUR *goes off to join them.*)

1ST VOICE   No job, nothing to do
No money, on the Bru   Repeat

2ND VOICE   No job after school
No future that's the rule   Repeat

ALL   Unemployment. Unemployment.

3RD VOICE   'O' Levels. 'A' levels. 'X' 'Y' 'Z' Levels.
'O' Levels. 'A' levels. 'X' 'Y' 'Z' Levels.

ALL   Unemployment. Unemployment.

(*Then a mixture of all the chants simultaneously rising in volume.*)

KATE *puts her hands over her ears. Shouts 'Stop!'*

Scene Four

Mid-March. SANDRA *and* MAUREEN *enter, followed by* TOMMY.

SANDRA   You told Johnnie's probation officer? Are ye out of yer friggin' mind?

She begins to do MAUREEN's *hair.* TOMMY *sits watching and reading a magazine.*

MAUREEN   I didn't know what else to do. I don't want him put away. I can't watch him all the time. When I'm here I never know if he's at school or roamin' the streets. She's nice, Claudia. She cares what happens til us.

SANDRA   She cares about keepin' her job. They all do.

MAUREEN   No, she's different, like Kate.

SANDRA   A do-gooder.

KATE *comes in, listens. They don't see her.*

TOMMY   Doin' her bit fer the poor. It's her job.

MAUREEN   She does a whole lot more for us she doesn't get paid fer doin'.

TOMMY   An' then goes back til her posh house up the Malone Road. If she's so liberated, why does she still live there with her ma instead of roun' here like us.

KATE   Because I'm lazy, that's why. My mother runs the house, and that leaves me free to run this place. It suits both of us.

MAUREEN   There's nuthin' wrong with livin' in a nice house. You mind yer own business, Tommy.

SANDRA   How many lives in your house, Kate?

KATE   Just the two of us. My father's dead. My two brothers are married.

SANDRA   I wish some of our ones would go off an' get married. There's ten of us an' three bedrooms. Ye can call nuthin' yer own.

TOMMY   If Arthur wins ask him to buy ye a big house in the country.

MAUREEN   I wonder how he's gettin' on?

TOMMY   It'll be all over by now. Sorry son, if the army says you were joyridin' that's good enough for us. No compensation.

KATE   He has a good case, you know. That solicitor
wouldn't have taken him on if he hadn't thought he
might win.

TOMMY   Sure, they get paid anyway, win or lose or draw.
They'll take anybody on.

ARTHUR *comes in. He is wearing a suit.* SANDRA *and*
TOMMY *fall about laughing.*

SANDRA Get him. Man from C an' A.

TOMMY   Where did ye get that outfit?

SANDRA His ma's been shoplifting again.

KATE   Leave him alone you lot. You look very nice Arthur.

SANDRA He looks like a tailor's dummy.

TOMMY   He looks like yer man, Yorkie.

KATE   Who's Yorkie?

SANDRA The Secretary of State. Big, rich an' thick. Well,
you're big an' yer thick, Arthur, but are ye rich?

ARTHUR *says nothing. Slowly takes off his tie.*

TOMMY   I knew ye wouldn't get nuthin'.

SANDRA He's smirkin'. He got somethin'.

TOMMY   Did ye?

SANDRA Look at his face.

ARTHUR You are now lookin' at the most illegible bachelor
in West Belfast.

TOMMY   How much did yer get?

ARTHUR *takes twenty Benson & Hedges from his pocket.*
(Normally the teenagers have tens of cheap cigarettes.)
He slowly counts out five cigarettes onto a table.

MAUREEN Five . . . five hundred pounds?

TOMMY   You got yer costs.

ARTHUR *shakes his head. Places another two cigarettes*
on the table.

SANDRA Jeesus, he got seven thousand, (ARTHUR *grins.*) Ye
did, didn't ye?

ARTHUR *shakes his head.*

SANDRA   Well, what then?

ARTHUR   I got seventy. (*There is a stunned silence.*) Seventy friggin' thousand pounds!

TOMMY   I don't believe ye.

SANDRA   Yer a lyin' hound.

ARTHUR   Hand on my heart an' hope to die.

MAUREEN   It's a fortune.

KATE   Well done, Arthur.

ARTHUR   I done nuthin'. It was the solicitor. He was brilliant, like the fella in the big picture. I mean it was all dead borin' at first, statements from witnesses an' hospital reports fulla big words. I couldn't make out the half of it, an' then the oul solicitor gets up and tells the court about the oul steel plate an' the hair not growin' an' the headaches, an' how my social life's ruined with the scars an' the limp . . . I never let on you were mad about me anyway, Sandra . . . I tell ye, he was that good he nearly had me in tears, I was that sorry fer myself.

MAUREEN   Seventy thousand pounds.

ARTHUR   I always hoped I'd get somethin', a couple of thousand maybe, an' then the day when I heard him talkin' I thought, they're gonna give me more, maybe ten, an' then the judge said seventy . . . I thought I was hearin' things.

KATE   You deserve it, Arthur, every penny and more. It sounds like a lot of money, but it has to do you for a lifetime.

SANDRA   Where is it? The money? Are Securicar waitin' at the front door?

ARTHUR   They don't give ye the loot in a suitcase, Sandra. You're as bad as my da. He thought he was gonna walk out of the court like Al Capone. Seventy G's in used notes.

TOMMY Do they give ye a cheque or what?

ARTHUR They give me nuthin'. It goes intil a trust till my eighteenth birthday.

SANDRA There's always a catch.

ARTHUR That's what my da said. You shoulda seen his face when he heard he wasn't gettin' his hands on it. When we come outa the court he puts his arm roun' my shoulders an' he says, 'Arthur son, you'll see me an' your mother right, won't ye? All them sleepless nights we sat up in the hospital prayin' for ye.' My ma sat up in the hospital, he did his prayin' in the pub. I never remember my da puttin' his arm roun' me before the day.

TOMMY It's a wonder he let ye out of his sight.

SANDRA Did they not give ye nuthin' in advance?

ARTHUR No.

SANDRA I never thought ye'd get it, but I thought if ye did we'd all get a drink outa it anyway.

KATE I knew he'd win.

She produces a bottle of champagne from her bag.

ARTHUR Is that real?

KATE The real McCoy.

SANDRA Where'd ye nick it?

KATE The Forum Hotel. I won it, at a supper dance.

MAUREEN In a raffle like?

KATE Tombola. I think you should open it, Arthur.

ARTHUR I've always wanted to open a bottle of champagne.

KATE You just turn this until the cork comes up . . .

SANDRA Here, it pops out, doesn't it? Quick, Maureen, cups. Arthur, wait a minute it'll spill all over the place.

MAUREEN *and* SANDRA *run to the kitchen, get cups, the cork pops. They catch the champagne.*

KATE To Arthur.

TEENAGERS Arthur!

They taste it.

TOMMY So that's what it's like.

MAUREEN It's different from what I thought . . .

SANDRA It's diabolical.

ARTHUR I like it.

SANDRA They seen ye comin' Kate. It's like fizzy dishwater.

TOMMY Somebody gettin' rid of their oul cheap muck in a raffle.

ARTHUR I like it.

KATE Actually it is one of the best champagnes.

MAUREEN Like the pop stars drink?

KATE Yes.

ARTHUR I like it.

TOMMY What does it cost, if ye were buyin' it?

KATE Around twenty pounds a bottle.

SANDRA Yer friggin' jokin'.

ARTHUR I knew it was good. It's like the difference between saute potatoes an' chips.

SANDRA Saute potatoes *is* chips, undercooked.

ARTHUR No it's not.

SANDRA Yes it is, unless you're doin' it wrong. An' somebody puttin' a fancy name on it doesn't make it better, just different an' more dear.

TOMMY (*admiringly*): Sandra, I wish you would join the Party.

SANDRA What for? To end up typin' letters fer wankers like you?

MAUREEN It gets nicer, the more ye drink.

ARTHUR Could anybody lend us a fiver till pay day? Only I would like to buy yiz all a drop of what ye fancy.

SANDRA Seventy thousand friggin' quid, and he's lookin' a sub fer a six pack.

MAUREEN What are ye gonna do with all that money, Arthur?

ARTHUR	I have plans, baby, I have plans.
KATE	Have you any plans for tonight?
SANDRA	It's Wednesday, nobody roun' here has any readies on a Wednesday.
TOMMY	Arthur's credit'll be good in the pub. His da'll be drinkin' on the slate already on the strength of what's to come.
KATE	Do you fancy coming up to my house, the four of you? I'll supply the drinks and Arthur can cook the supper.
SANDRA	Your house?
KATE	Yes. (*There is an awkward pause.*) It was just a thought.
MAUREEN	I'd like to go.
TOMMY	Your ma wouldn't want the like of us in your house.
KATE	My mother's staying with her sister for a few days.
MAUREEN	You all on yer own like, Kate?
KATE	Look, you don't have to . . . I just said it on the spur of the moment . . .
ARTHUR	You got a big posh kitchen, Kate?
KATE	Yes.
ARTHUR	An' ye'd let me cook in it?
KATE	I'd love you to cook in it, I hate cooking.
ARTHUR	Yer on. Can I cook anything I want?
KATE	Within reason.
TOMMY	What had ye in mind?
ARTHUR	It'll be a surprise.
SANDRA	Your food's always a friggin' surprise.
ARTHUR	Ye don' have to come if ye don't want to.
SANDRA	Might as well. I've nuthin' better to do.
KATE	Tommy? You want to see how the other half live?
TOMMY	I know how the other half live.

SANDRA	He read it in a magazine.
TOMMY	Have you got a library?
KATE	I've got a lot of books.
TOMMY	Can I look at them?
SANDRA	He wants to colour in the pictures.
KATE	Of course you can look at them.
SANDRA	Don't lend him none, he'll flog them.
MAUREEN	What time'll we come, only I'll hafta make our Johnnie his tea first.
SANDRA	Why can't the wee bugger make his own tea?
KATE	Whatever time you like. Oh, and Arthur, you'll need money to buy in the ingredients for the surprise meal. Do you mind? I'll be here still after six. I won't have time to go shopping. (*She hands him some money.*) You'd better go now before the supermarket closes.
SANDRA	I'm goin' with him, he'll go mad an' buy a lot of oul daft rubbish.
ARTHUR	Hey Sandra, I've always wanted to push a trolley roun' the supermarket with you.
SANDRA	Well, enjoy it the day. It'll be the first an' last time.
	They exit.
TOMMY	Do you want me to get you some booze Kate? Only I know a place where you can get it cheap.
KATE	Eh, no thanks Tommy, I have some at home.
TOMMY	Next time yer stockin' up, give us a shout.
	He exits.
MAUREEN	Do you know what must be the best thing about having money? Never havin' to go to the Social Security. I hate that place. Do you think I'll get a job when my time's up here?
KATE	You're hard working, conscientious, no police record. You have a high chance.
MAUREEN	You've no chance when the Job Centre find out yer from Divis Flats.

KATE   I'm hoping to organise a typing course. Would you
             like to do it?

MAUREEN   Me work in an office?

KATE   Why not?

MAUREEN   The only office work I'm likely to get is washin'
             floors.

KATE   You can do better than that.

MAUREEN   It wouldn't bother me. I just want a job. Any sort of
             a job. I don't care what it is. I wanta earn my own
             money, never stand in no more queues pleadin'
             poverty. Never have to fill in no more forms.
             'Where's your father? – I don't know. Where's your
             mother? – In the looney bin.' I'll spend a year here
             and at the end of it I'll be back where I started off.
             No job, no money. Arthur spends a year in the
             hospital, an' at the end of it he gets seventy
             thousand pounds . . . I wonder would the army
             like to shoot me?

             Pause.

             Offstage the song 'Children of Divis Flats'.

             Blackout.

ACT TWO

Scene One

KATE*'s house after the meal.* ARTHUR *sings 'Oh I was out walking'.*

ARTHUR   (*sings straight*): Oh I was out walking outside Divis
Flats
Where the happiest tenants are surely the rats
Where we all breathe asbestos and no one is well
I walked down the steps and I tripped and fell
And I never knew when I had my fall
The Executive owned the steps, and the D.O.E.
owned the wall.

I was took to the doctor all aching and sore
My ankle is swollen, can't walk anymore
He gave me some tablets and we had a talk
They made me feel dizzy, I still cannot walk.

ALL   And he never knew, when I had my fall
The Executive owned the steps, and the D.O.E.
owned the wall.

ARTHUR   (*parodying the worst type of Irish nasal country and
western singer*):

My mother was raging, she went for a claim
She looked up a number and solicitor's name
She told him my story and he was all ears
But he shook his head sadly 'This claim will take years.'

ALL   Pity he didn't know when he had his fall
The Executive owned the steps, and the D.O.E. the
wall.

ARTHUR   It's now five years later, and the claim's still not paid
There's wrangles and tangles, no settlement made
There's 'phone calls and letters, they argue and talk
I'm stuck in the flat now; I still cannot walk.

ALL   And nobody cares about you at all
When the Executive owns the steps, and the D.O.E.
owns the wall.
And nobody cares about you at all

When the Executive owns the steps, and the D.O.E. owns the wall.

They all cheer, applaud. KATE *and* ARTHUR *go off to the kitchen.*

MAUREEN   It was lovely, wasn't it. Arthur's awful good at the cookin'.

SANDRA   Do ye want more wine?

MAUREEN   Leave some fer Kate an' Arthur.

TOMMY   Plenty more where that come from. I wonder what the poor people are doin' these days?

SANDRA   I thought the party didn't approve of this sorta livin'.

TOMMY   We want everybody to live like this, not just the privileged few.

SANDRA   Oh aye? An' who's gonna do the dirty work while everybody's livin' like this?

TOMMY   Machines.

SANDRA   You've been readin' them star-wars comics again.

TOMMY   Some of the ornaments in this house would feed a family fer a fortnight. (*He picks up a photo in a silver frame.*) Here, look at this . . . to Kate, all my love, Roger. Must be her fella.

SANDRA   Give us a dekko . . . here, he's not bad lookin' . . . for a Roger.

MAUREEN   He's lovely lookin'.

SANDRA   A wee screw.

MAUREEN   You make everything cheap so ye do.

TOMMY   Nuthin' cheap about this place.

MAUREEN   Can the two of yiz not just enjoy yourselves. It's lovely here.

SANDRA   She'll be day dreamin' all day the morra.

MAUREEN   There's nuthin' wrong with day dreamin'.

SANDRA   There is if you believe in it. None of us is never gonna live nowhere but them stinkin' flats . . . unless we emigrate . . .

TOMMY	Nobody'd have us.
MAUREEN	If you could live anywhere in the world, where would ye go?
SANDRA	Dunno, but I'll tell ye where I wouldn't go, friggin' America. Once was enough.
MAUREEN	You don't know what side yer bread's buttered on. You got a free holiday, an' all ye ever done was complain about it. Half the school wanted to go, an' you were the one got picked.
SANDRA	I never had no luck.
MAUREEN	Vera Cosgrove went one year an' she thought it was brilliant.
SANDRA	Vera Cosgrove's a lick.
MAUREEN	I'm tryin' to get our Johnnie on one of them trips.
SANDRA	With his record? Are ye jokin'?
MAUREEN	They haven't said no yet.
TOMMY	They will. They only take the well-behaved deservin' poor.
MAUREEN	They must be considerin' him. They give me a whole lotta stuff to read.

She rummages in her bag, produces some leaflets.

TOMMY	Let me see . . . (*He reads.*) The Tennessee Summer Holiday Program for Irish Children . . . was that where you went, Sandra?
SANDRA	I was in North Carolina. Must be the most borin' place on God's earth. They never stop prayin'.

KATE *and* ARTHUR *come in carrying liqueurs.*

ARTHUR	I told Kate she'd get done fer aidin' an' abettin' under-age drinkin', but she says this is a special occasion.
KATE	And I'm running you all home afterwards to make sure you don't get picked up.
MAUREEN	It's lovely roun' here. No army nor police nor nuthin'.

TOMMY	No need. They don't make petrol bombs roun' here, just money.
SANDRA	(*sniffing the liqueur*): What's this?
KATE	It's a coffee liqueur.
	SANDRA *swallows a large mouthful, coughs, splutters.*
SANDRA	Jeesus!
ARTHUR	Yer supposed to sip it slow, ye ignoramous.
MAUREEN	(*sipping hers*): It's lovely.
SANDRA	It beats glue.
KATE	Do you sniff glue, Sandra?
SANDRA	Nigh an' again.
KATE	Why?
SANDRA	Why do flies eat shite?
TOMMY	Because they can't afford gin and tonic.
KATE	Do you all do it?
ARTHUR	I usta. After the accident I never bothered no more.
SANDRA	He's afraid it'll rust the oul steel plate.
MAUREEN	I never done it. It's the road to nowhere.
SANDRA	You never do nuthin'. That's why yer so miserable all the time.
	TOMMY *is reading the leaflets about America.*
TOMMY	You'd think we were refugees. Have you read these, Maureen?
MAUREEN	Only some of them. I only got them the day.
TOMMY	Listen to this . . . 'You will love America. You will be coming to a peaceful place, a happy place, a safe place. No rioting, no shooting, no bombs, no soldiers.'
SANDRA	No hope . . .
TOMMY	'Things you should know about the American people . . .'
SANDRA	When they're not talkin' they're eatin'.
TOMMY	'Americans bathe or shower regularly, at least

several times a week, or even every day. Your hosts will expect you to do this too. You will find American showers a lot of fun.'

SANDRA See what I mean? They think we're still washin' under the pump in the yard.

TOMMY (*reading from the leaflet*): An' they think we might not of heard of foods like baked potatoes, mustard, cucumber an' spaghetti . . .

KATE Let me see that. What is it?

SANDRA Free holidays fer the poor an' needy.

KATE (*reading*): 'In America we call baps, dinner rolls . . . ' Is this a joke?

SANDRA It's a friggin' insult.

KATE (*reading*): Many Americans are of Irish descent, so you will find some familiar foods such as spam and Campbells Scotch Broth.'

SANDRA *pretends to be sick.*

ARTHUR My ma says they usta send food parcels over here durin' the war. Now they're taking the kids over there to eat their leftovers.

KATE We'll have to send you over, Arthur. Teach them how to cook.

SANDRA When I was in America, the Bible-thumper I stopped with says one day . . . little girl, we are going to give you a special treat. We're taking you to a real Chinese restaurant. Won't that be exciting? She got all huffed when I told her that we've more friggin' Chinese restaurants than chip shops in Belfast. An' anyway, I hate Chinese food.

ARTHUR I didn't see you turnin' up yer nose at my sweet an' sour pork the night.

SANDRA I knew what was in it. I was with ye when ye bought the stuff. See in them restaurants? They cook dogs an' cats an' dead pigeons, so they do.

MAUREEN They do not.

SANDRA They do, it's a well-known fact.

TOMMY   I'll tell ye somthin' that's not a well-known fact . . .

SANDRA   The Pope's doin' a line with Maggie Thatcher.

ARTHUR   What's the fastest thing on two wheels?

SANDRA   The Pope ridin' up the Shankill on a bicycle. What's the fastest thing on two legs?

ARTHUR   Ian Paisley runnin' after him.

TOMMY   What language is spoken by most of the people in Ireland?

SANDRA   Are you talkin' or chewin' a brick or what Tommy?

ARTHUR   I dunno that one.

TOMMY   It's not a stupid joke. It's a question. What do most people speak here?

ARTHUR   English.

TOMMY   An' what's the next language what most people speak here?

SANDRA   Jail Irish.

TOMMY   No, not even school Irish.

ARTHUR   What then?

TOMMY   Chinese.

ARTHUR   Yer head's cut.

TOMMY   It's true.

ARTHUR   How do ye know?

SANDRA   Picked his nose an' it fell out.

TOMMY   I read it in a magazine. There are so many Chinese restaurants here that Chinese is the second language of Ireland. Do ye not think that's an amazin' fact?

SANDRA   No.

TOMMY   I don't understand you, Sandra.

SANDRA   You don't understand me?

TOMMY   Yer bright an' yer stupid all at the same time.

SANDRA   An' you were definitely a forceps delivery.

TOMMY   An' you were born up an entry.

SANDRA   At least I know who my da is.

MAUREEN	(*screams*): Stop it. Tell them to stop it, Kate!
	They all stare at her.
KATE	Maureen?
MAUREEN	They're spoilin' it. They always spoil it . . . everything nice . . . makin' a joke of it . . . makin' it rotten . . . I don't like dirty talk . . . yiz spoil everything so ye do . . .
	She runs out. KATE *goes after her. There is silence for a moment.*
TOMMY	What's up with her these days? Every time you look roun' she's cryin' about somethin'.
SANDRA	It's that head-the-ball Johnnie. If he was my brother I'd kick his friggin' head in.
ARTHUR	People keep kickin' his head in. It makes no difference.
TOMMY	He's addicted til it. He wasn't even ten the first time he went joyridin'. Him an' another wee lad. They were that small, one of them had til turn the steerin' wheel, while the other one worked the foot pedals. An oul green van it was. They drove it intil a brick wall an' scarpered. The wall an' the car was wrecked, an' they got out without a mark on them.
SANDRA	Jammy wee buggers.
ARTHUR	There'll be more than a mark on him if the Provos get the houl of him. They gave Frankie Devlin a terrible hammerin'.
TOMMY	They wouldn't do that to Johnnie. He's only twelve.
SANDRA	It's freelance thieves they're beatin' up these days. You'd better start stealin' for them instead of for yerself Tommy, or ye'll be gettin' yer knees broke with the hurley bat.
	KATE *comes back with* MAUREEN.
MAUREEN	I'm sorry. I dunno what got intil me. I musta drunk that liqueur too quick.
	There is an awkward silence.

KATE	Shall I make some coffee?
MAUREEN	I'll hafta go soon. The woman next door said she'd keep an eye on Johnnie, but she goes to bed early so she does. I don't wanta spoil yer night out. I'll go home on the bus.
KATE	You'll do nothing of the sort. It's time we were all going.
ARTHUR	Aye, I need my beauty sleep.
SANDRA	You need a body transplant.
MAUREEN	We never done the dishes or nuthin' Kate.
KATE	There's no need. We have a dishwasher.
ARTHUR	We have a dishwasher in our house too. My granny.
SANDRA	Ha ha.
KATE	Come on, let's go.
MAUREEN	It was lovely Kate, thanks very much.

KATE, MAUREEN *and* TOMMY *exit.* SANDRA *goes to follow them, stops, drains a couple of glasses.*

ARTHUR	Sandra?
SANDRA	What?
ARTHUR	Put it back.
SANDRA	What?
ARTHUR	Put it back.
SANDRA	Ye want me to spit it intil the bottle?
ARTHUR	The bottle in yer bag. Put it back.
SANDRA	What bottle?
ARTHUR	I seen ye, earlier on.
SANDRA	They put eyes in the back of yer head up in the hospital?
ARTHUR	Put it back.
SANDRA	They'll never miss it.
ARTHUR	You don't steal from yer own.
SANDRA	She's not one of us.
ARTHUR	She's as near as makes no difference.

SANDRA	She's a pain.
ARTHUR	She's a lady.
SANDRA	An' you're plannin' to be a gentleman now yer rich?
ARTHUR	Put it back.
SANDRA	You know the only reason you got the compensation? 'Cause you've got no record. An' that's only because you never got caught. You're no better than me.
ARTHUR	I never said I was.
SANDRA	You fancy her. You do, don't ye?
ARTHUR	Put the bottle back.

SANDRA *takes the bottle from her bag. Puts it on the table.*

SANDRA	Put it back yerself.

ARTHUR *replaces the bottle.*

SANDRA	Honest Arthur the boss's friend. You'll be gettin' religion next.
ARTHUR	You'll be gettin' jail next time yer caught.
SANDRA	What's that to you?
ARTHUR	Nuthin'.
SANDRA	If I do you can always bail me out with all that money yer gettin'.

ARTHUR *grabs her. Kisses her clumsily. She pushes him away.*

SANDRA	Get off, scarface.

She walks out. ARTHUR *stands, looking slightly forlorn for a moment, then shrugs.*

ARTHUR	Cheeky get.

He looks around the room.

ARTHUR	Won't be long til I can afford a place like this.
SONG:	Damp, Damp, Damp, Damp, Damp, Damp, Damp, Damp.
	Mushrooms on my ceiling, drips on the wall

Steaming soaking bedclothes, blackened flaky halls
Spiders on the woodwork, mould on the clothes
Children lying in the beds, they're nearly froze.

I went to the Housing Executive, to explain my
situation   -
I said 'I've got terrible damp'
They said 'It's only condensation'.

No, it's damp, damp, damp, damp, damp, damp,
damp, damp.

Toilets overflowing, carpets all wet
If you think that's bad, take a look at that.

It's rats, rats, rats, rats, rats, rats, rats, rats.

Rats will bite your nose off, then just slink away
They're living in our bedrooms, they are here to
stay.
Rats are full of poison, carry germs and fleas
You don't know what you could catch – some
horrible disease.
Old Mother Hubbard went to the cupboard to get a
piece of bread
She put her hand in the breadbin, and found
something else instead
AUGH!
She found rats, rats, rats, rats, rats, rats, rats, rats.
They bring their families with them for breakfast,
lunch and tea
I am paying heat and rent, but they are living free.

Every little tiny rat is out to get your child and cat!

Damp, damp, damp, damp, damp, damp, damp,
damp.

Scene Two

The Lagan Mill. End of March.

KATE, *sitting reading an official letter. She phones*
CLAUDIA.

KATE   Hello Claudia? It's Kate, look I'm sorry, but I can't
meet you for lunch today, I've a meeting with the
hierarchy later this morning, and I've been asked to
partake of a civil service lunch afterwards. Cold cuts
and cheap white wine to cushion the bribe . . . I'm
being manipulated into having an open day. You
know the sort of thing – important official comes in,
swans around making patronising comments about
the kids' work, pats them all on their dear little well-
scrubbed heads, and hopefully goes off feeling
righteous enough to recommend funding for
another year . . . no, of course I know it's not
ultimately up to me . . . it's just that I would like
to have the courage to say 'Stuff your open day and
your pompous V.I.P. I will not have the kids here
paraded out like a chimps' tea party. Give them the
bloody money as a right not a privilege for good
behaviour.' But I won't. I'll make the nominal
protest, which will be noted in the minutes (black
mark, Kate) and then I'll be grown up and
reasonable and will organise the event to perfection
(gold star, Kate) . . . Claudia, you don't have to
justify my reasons for agreeing. I've become very
adept at doing that for myself. I'm just saying out
loud what I want to do, before I agree to what I
have to do . . . God, isn't it a long time since we
sang 'We Shall Overcome' and believed it . . .
Listen, do you fancy going to the Opera House this
evening? I've got complimentary tickets, and Roger's
working late. Oh . . . no, no, it's all right I'll take
mother . . . have a good time. I'll give you a call
next week . . . Thanks, bye.

She replaces the receiver. SANDRA *comes in.* KATE *looks at her watch.*

KATE I don't believe it. Were you up all night?

SANDRA We were all up all night. They got Tommy. Four o'clock this mornin'.

KATE Who got Tommy?

SANDRA The great lads he's always bummin' he's so friendly with.

KATE What happened?

SANDRA They broke both his hands. Stupid bugger. I warned him, we all did. You don't steal round here. You do it in the big shops in the town. They don't mind that.

KATE They broke his hands?

SANDRA They'da done worse, only his ma run intil the street, squealin'. Next thing the army was in. They used it as an excuse to take the flats apart. You wanna see the state of the place. Glass everywhere.

KATE There was nothing about it on the news this morning.

SANDRA Our windows is always gettin' broke. It's not news. Who cares about the army smashin' up the windows and the doors in Divis Flats. The bloody place is fallin' to bits anyway. Walls streamin' with water, toilets overflowin', rubbish chutes that don't work. If the rats an' the bugs don't get ye, the asbestos will . . . or the police, or the army, or the I.R.A. . . . who cares?

KATE Did you see Tommy?

SANDRA No. But I heard him. Pigs! An' they're supposed to be on our side.

KATE Sandra, you're worn out. Go back home and get some sleep.

SANDRA And get my pay docked? Are you jokin'? I'm down the best part of a pound already this week.

MAUREEN *comes in.*

MAUREEN	Did she tell you?
KATE	Yes. Did you see Tommy?
MAUREEN	Johnnie an' me hid under the bed till it was all over.
SANDRA	Did they not come in til your place?
MAUREEN	Somebody hammered on the door, but we never let on ourselves an' they went away.
SANDRA	Couldn'ta been the Brits. They'da broke the door down.
MAUREEN	Is Arthur not in yet? I'm dyin' fer a cuppa tea. They've cut off the water as well as the electric, Kate.
KATE	Who?
MAUREEN	It happens all the time.
SANDRA	Arthur got picked up.
MAUREEN	What for?
SANDRA	He came out onto the balcony to see what was goin' on, an' they had him in the back of the landrover before his feet had time to touch the ground.
KATE	He wasn't doing anything?
SANDRA	Jeesus, Kate, you might as well live on the moon fer all ye know. You don't have to be doin' nuthin'. Ye just hafta be there. He's a stupid get, Arthur. He's got picked up like that before. One look at that face of his an' they haul him in fer questioning.
MAUREEN	It's not right.
SANDRA	His solicitor'll have him out before lunchtime. He's used to it. Can I make some tea Kate?
KATE	Yes, of course you can. I'll go and see who's in.
MAUREEN	There'll not be many in the day. They'll all be sleepin' or standin' aroun' talking about it . . .
KATE	Did anybody else from in here get picked up?
SANDRA	That wee lad Oliver from the joinery section. He was lobbin' milk bottles at the Brits. He got three of

them before they grabbed him. He's dead good. He
plays darts.

KATE   Anybody else?

SANDRA   Not from in here. The rest they lifted was on the
dole. Can I make a bitta toast as well, Kate? Only
I'm starvin'.

KATE   Yes.

She exits.

SANDRA   She takes it all dead serious, doesn't she? Do ye
want toast, Maureen?

MAUREEN   No, just a cuppa tea.

SANDRA   How did ye keep your Johnnie in? He loves all that.
Did ye nail his feet til the floor?

MAUREEN   I give him a pound.

SANDRA   Yer mad. He'll be out buyin' glue with it.

MAUREEN   He doesn't do that no more.

SANDRA   Like he doesn't joyride no more? Wise up, Maureen.
He's wired to the moon that wee lad.

MAUREEN   You usta go in the back of the cars.

SANDRA   I grew out of it.

MAUREEN   Our Johnnie's grew out of it too. (SANDRA *gives her a
long look.*) . . . I asked him why he keeps doin' it.
He says it's a laugh.

SANDRA   It usta be a laugh. It stopped bein' funny the day
the Brits stopped shoutin' halt an' opened fire. Do
ye know Geordie Quinn? They got him right there.
(*She points to below her navel.*) He showed me his
stitches. Another two inches an' he'd a got the
D.S.O. Why do ye not want any toast?

MAUREEN   I'm not hungry.

SANDRA   You ate nuthin' these days. What's up with ye?

MAUREEN   What do ye mean?

SANDRA   Suit yerself. Aw, frig there's no milk.

MAUREEN   The crate's at the front door. I'll get it.

SANDRA	It's heavy. I'll get it.
	There is a pause.
MAUREEN	What am I gonna do, Sandra?
SANDRA	What are ye askin' me for?
MAUREEN	You asked me. How did ye know?
SANDRA	I've two older sisters. I've seen that look. Candles to the virgin an' promises never to do it again. How far gone are ye?
MAUREEN	Four week an' three days.
SANDRA	You could still be all right.
MAUREEN	I went to Boots. I'm not all right.
SANDRA	Have ye told him?
MAUREEN	He's away home for a month. He's a student.
SANDRA	Away home where?
MAUREEN	I met him in the Botanic Gardens.
SANDRA	Where?
MAUREEN	The Botanic Gardens. It's behind the university.
SANDRA	I only know roun' here. What were ye doin' away over there?
MAUREEN	It's not far from the hospital. I go an' look at the plants sometimes. There's a plam house and a tropical ravine and the Ulster Museum. It's lovely. Ye should go sometime.
SANDRA	Is that where ye done it?
MAUREEN	He lives in a flat, roun' the corner. Not like our flats. In an old house with a garden. It's lovely.
SANDRA	Jeesus, you musta been at the back of the queue when they were handin' out the brains.
MAUREEN	What am I gonna do, Sandra?
SANDRA	How would I know?
MAUREEN	What would you do?
SANDRA	I don't do it. Nobody's never gonna catch me like that.

MAUREEN	I thought . . .
SANDRA	Ye thought what?
MAUREEN	Nuthin'.
SANDRA	You see fellas? They talk about ye if ye do it, an' they make it up if ye don't.
MAUREEN	They'll all talk about me.
SANDRA	This road's hivin' with kids. One more won't make no difference.
MAUREEN	It'll look different.
SANDRA	What way different?
MAUREEN	He's not from roun' here.
SANDRA	Tommy's da wasn't from roun' here. My ma says he was a half-caste what come roun' the doors sellin' floor polish. She says that's why Tommy has a bit of a tan all the year roun'.
MAUREEN	They'll take Johnnie away when they find out.
SANDRA	They're gonna take Johnnie away anyway . . . Has he any money, Cairo Fred or whoever he is? You can make him pay. It's the law.
MAUREEN	We only done it twice.
SANDRA	Once is enough. God but you're thick. I suppose he told you he loved you?
MAUREEN	He was lovely. He talks awful nice. Not like the ones round here. (SANDRA *rolls her eyes in disbelief.*) I'll get the milk.
SANDRA	I'll get the milk. You rest yer swelled ankles.
MAUREEN	His father's a prince or somethin'.
SANDRA	Aye, an' Tommy's da was Omar Sharif.

She exits. MAUREEN *looks down.*

| MAUREEN | There's nuthin' the matter with my ankles . . . (*She begins to work the knitting machine, stops, looks down.*) Don't heed her baby . . . he loves me . . . I know he does . . . he said he did . . . and he's a gentleman . . . (*She operates the knitting* |

machine again, stops.) We're gonna live in an old
house behind the university . . . and every day I'll
put you in your pram and wheel you round the
Botanic Gardens . . . a proper pram . . . Silver
Cross with big high wheels . . . and everybody'll
look at you, you'll be that beautiful . . . your
father's dark eyes an' your grannie's blonde hair
. . . (*She stops at the thought of her mother.* SANDRA
comes in, sets the milk down, watches and listens to
MAUREEN *who doesn't see her.*) Your granny was like
the sun . . . all golden . . . she lit up everything
she touched . . . she comes from the country and
got cooped up in the flats like a battery hen . . .
the day your granda went to England to look for
work, we were that miserable she took ma an'
Johnnie to the pictures . . . The Wizard of Oz . . .
it was lovely . . . an' the next day she bought
seven pot plants . . . seven . . . an' she put them
in a row on the kitchen window sill an' she said . .
. 'They'll all flower except for the fourth one. That
one has to stay green.' And she wouldn't tell us
why. 'Wait and see' she said . . . 'Wait and see.'
We watched an' we waited for a while an' nuthin'
happened, an' we lost interest. Didn't even notice
them anymore. And then one day I come in from
school an' all the pot plants had flowers except the
fourth one, just like she said. (*She smiles and counts
on her fingers.*) Red, orange, yellow, green, blue,
indigo, violet . . . 'See' she said, 'we have a rainbow
on our window sill.' (*She looks round, sees* SANDRA.)
You come in that day . . . do you remember?

SANDRA   You an' your Johnnie were dancin' round the
kitchen singin' 'Somewhere over the rainbow' an'
your mother was laughin' an' she said 'We're all mad
in this family, Sandra. Some day the men in the
white coats are gonna come in and take us all away.'

MAUREEN   Our Johnnie doesn't remember it. I asked him the
other day.

SANDRA   It was a long time ago.

MAUREEN   He's the spittin' image of her. Blond curly hair, blue
          eyes. Like one of them cherubs in the stained-glass
          windows. How can he look so like her and be so
          different? She only had to smile at you and you felt
          warm . . . Johnnie's light doesn't warm . . . it
          burns . . . it burns . . . and I can't get anywhere
          near him . . . (*She is incoherent, sobbing.*) And I
          don't know what to do . . .

SANDRA   Maureen, don't, you'll make yourself sick . . .

MAUREEN   You mean mad . . . like her . . .

SANDRA   No I don't. Come on Maureen . . . into the loo . . .
          wash your face an' I'll make ye a cuppa tea . . .
          come on . . . you don't want anybody to see you
          like this . . . you know the way they talk . . .
          come on . . .

          She looks as if she wants to touch MAUREEN, *but can't.*
          MAUREEN *walks, dazed, towards the exit, turns back
          to* SANDRA.

MAUREEN   Sure you won't tell nobody . . .

SANDRA   Cross my heart and hope to die.

          She walks off. SANDRA *follows her.*

                        Scene Three

          Open day at the Lagan Mill. Mid-April.

          TOMMY *(his hands in plaster) is sitting watching*
          SANDRA *who is writing on a large sheet of paper with
          a felt-tip pen. A radio is playing, very loudly,
          'Alternative Ulster' by the Belfast punk group Stiff
          Little Fingers.* KATE *is rushing about. She turns the
          radio down. Exits.* ARTHUR *comes in carrying
          prepared food. He grins at* TOMMY.

ARTHUR   Hiya, Tommy. Clap your hands. How're ye doing?

TOMMY   Okay.

SANDRA   It's one way of stoppin' smokin', eh Tommy? Here

ye are Arthur.

She pins up a sign. 'Get Your Non-Sectarian Nosh Here.' Sits down and begins writing again.

TOMMY   They'll make ye take that down. (SANDRA *shrugs.*) What time are the big nobs comin' in?

ARTHUR   They're comin' for lunch an' then they're havin' a look roun' the sections.

TOMMY   An' then they'll pat yiz all on the head an' tell ye what good children yiz all are.

ARTHUR   There's some real big nob comin' in. He's a Royal or somethin'.

TOMMY   He's not a Royal. He's from the Home Office. They're interested in this scheme. Yous should be boycottin' his visit, not feedin' his face.

ARTHUR   Sandra, you're supposed to be helpin' me.

SANDRA   In a minute. Houl yer horses.

ARTHUR   What are ye doin'?

SANDRA   Makin' an Irish welcome for the English civil servant.

KATE comes in. Turns the radio off.

KATE   Does anybody know where Maureen is? Sandra?

SANDRA   Haven't seen her.

KATE   It's not like her. She's never late.

SANDRA   What do ye think, Kate?

She holds up another sign. It says 'Never Mind What The Papers Say. We All Love Ye, Conn.'

KATE   Who's Conn?

SANDRA   The man from the Home Office.

KATE   His name is Jeremy Saunders. Who's Conn?

They all grin.

KATE   Okay. I'm a thick middle-class moron. Would somebody like to explain it to me?

MAUREEN rushes in. She is carrying a Marks and Spencer's carrier bag.

MAUREEN	Sorry I'm late Kate.
KATE	That's all right. Are you all right?
MAUREEN	I had a message to do this mornin'. Forgot to tell ye.
KATE	Are you sure you're all right?
MAUREEN	Why shouldn't I be all right?
KATE	Do you know who Conn is?
MAUREEN	Conn who?
ARTHUR	It's a name for any English Civil Servant.
TOMMY	It's short for constipation, the shite you can't get rid of.
KATE	Are you planning to pin that up?
SANDRA	They'll never know what it means, an' they'll be too polite to ask.
KATE	It would be really embarrassing if this scheme didn't get a second year's funding because an English civil servant was brighter than you lot thought.
TOMMY	I'm away. See yiz all later.
KATE	Are you not staying to heckle?
TOMMY	We're stagin' a demonstration.
KATE	Outside.
TOMMY	We're protestin' about Mr Jeremy Saunders bein' here. Do you know his da owns half of Cornwall or somewhere?
KATE	God give me strength.
TOMMY	You shoulda said no, Kate.
KATE	I didn't want this open day. I was told it had to take place. Will you tell the Party that I don't care if Jeremy Saunders' father owns all of Cornwall. All I care about is getting enough money to keep this place going for at least another year. While you lot are trying to change the face of the world, I am just trying to get the kids here through another rotten day.
TOMMY	Yer wrong, Kate.

KATE	I know I'm wrong. But it's the best I can think of till the revolution comes.
SANDRA	Yer both wrong. When we're all drawin' the pension there'll still be head-the-balls like him an' there'll still be well-meanin' people like you, an' nuthin' will be no different. Do ye know what this scheme is? It's a friggin' Government joyride. A good laugh for a year, an' then ye grow up.
KATE	Put your posters up, Sandra. If Mr Jeremy Saunders is intelligent enough to know what it means, he'll be too sophisticated to care.

She walks out. TOMMY *follows her.*

ARTHUR	Do ye know what they're talkin' about Maureen?
SANDRA	Maureen doesn't know what time of time it is. What's in the bag?
MAUREEN	None of your business. What's all the glasses for?
ARTHUR	Wine.
SANDRA	We get lectures about the demon drink, an' they can't manage a meal without a bottle of wine.
MAUREEN	Where's the wine?
ARTHUR	Kate has it hid away. She's no dozer.

SANDRA *looks in the Marks and Spencer's bag.*

MAUREEN	Put that down!
SANDRA	I was only lookin'.
MAUREEN	Well don't. Yer hands is all felt tip.
SANDRA	Well you show me then.
MAUREEN	Not now.
SANDRA	Arthur!
ARTHUR	What?
SANDRA	On yer bike!
ARTHUR	What?
SANDRA	Maureen wants to try on her new frock.
MAUREEN	I don't!
ARTHUR	I won't look.

SANDRA   Bugger off when yer told.

ARTHUR   I've a lot to do. Yiz have ten minutes.

SANDRA   Don't come back in till yer called.

ARTHUR *exits*.

SANDRA   Well, come on then. Let us see.

MAUREEN *takes an expensive matching outfit out of the bag. Jacket, skirt, trousers, top, shoes.*

SANDRA   You rob the meter or what?

MAUREEN   I've been savin' up since Christmas. I've always wanted this outfit. It was reduced in the sale. You can wear the skirt or the trousers with the jacket, swap them roun'.

SANDRA   Try it on.

MAUREEN   Kate might come in.

SANDRA   Kate hasn't got nuthin' we haven't got.

MAUREEN *takes off her skirt and shoes. Puts on the new jacket, skirt and shoes.*

MAUREEN   No mirror. Is it nice?

SANDRA   The jacket's awful big.

MAUREEN   It's the fashion. It's supposed to be big.

SANDRA   It would fit two. It'll come in handy later on . . . ach, fer God's sake, Maureen, I was only jokin'. Stop lookin' like a wet week all the time.

MAUREEN   I'm not sure about the colour. They had it in pink as well.

SANDRA   Ye can always get it changed.

MAUREEN   I want to wear it the day.

SANDRA   What for? Are ye hopin' Mr Saunders'll fall for ye an' offer ye a job in Stormont Castle?

KATE *comes in*.

KATE   Oh, that's nice Maureen. Is it new?

MAUREEN   Why shouldn't it be new?

KATE   No reason . . . I . . .

MAUREEN	I've as much right to new clothes as the next one, so I have.
KATE	You look lovely.
MAUREEN	I look a sight. It's too big.
	She takes the outfit off. Stuffs it back into the bag.
KATE	Careful. Don't crease it or they won't give you your money back.
	KATE *takes the clothes out, folds them, puts them back into the carrier bag.* ARTHUR *comes in.*
ARTHUR	Hey Kate, the Law's back. They want to see you.
KATE	They've already checked the building twice. What do they want now?
ARTHUR	They never said. I suppose when Jeremy Saunders comes in the place'll be crawlin' with them.
KATE	Mr Saunders will have his own heavies in tow. Would you two give Arthur a hand with the food? I won't be long.
ARTHUR	What about the wine?
KATE	They won't be here for a while. We'll open it later.
ARTHUR	The red should be opened in advance.
KATE	There's plenty of time.
	She exits.
SANDRA	Good try, Arthur.
ARTHUR	Do ye think they'll let us drink the leftovers?
SANDRA	Yer ever hopeful.
ARTHUR	Are ye not wearin' your new frock for them, Maureen?
MAUREEN	No.
	SANDRA *puts her finger into one of the bowls, tastes the contents.*
SANDRA	Jeesus, Arthur, what's this?
ARTHUR	Cheese dip.
SANDRA	It's revoltin'.

ARTHUR	Try this one.
SANDRA	What is it?
ARTHUR	Celery, date an' walnut salad.
SANDRA	I hate dates.
ARTHUR	Do ye like cooked ham?
SANDRA	It's all right.
ARTHUR	Well do ye think ye could stop complainin' an roll the ham up, put a cocktail stick through it an' sprinkle it with chopped parsley?
SANDRA	What for?
ARTHUR	Because it looks nicer that way, than lyin' flat on a plate.
SANDRA	They're gonna ate it, not take pictures of it.
ARTHUR	Maureen, will you do the ham? (*To* SANDRA.) You do the lettuce, it's all yer fit for.
SANDRA	Up yer nose Arthur.
	KATE *comes in.*
SANDRA	Hey Kate, do the Law know there's a suspect device in Arthur's potato salad?
KATE	Would the two of you go outside for a moment. I want to talk to Maureen.
SANDRA	What's up?
KATE	Just do as you're told!
ARTHUR	Is there somethin' wrong, Kate?
KATE	Just go.
SANDRA	Do as yer told and ye'll live long enough, Arthur.
	SANDRA *and* ARTHUR *leave.*
KATE	Is it true Maureen?
MAUREEN	Is what true?
KATE	I said I wanted to talk to you first. They gave me five minutes.
MAUREEN	How did they know it was me?
KATE	Oh Maureen, what got into you?

MAUREEN   How did they know?

KATE   When you ran out of the shop, there was a
policeman across the street. He recognised you. He
was in court the day Johnnie was put on probation.
They went to your home, and Johnnie told them
you were here.

MAUREEN   What's Johnnie doin' in the house? He should be at
school.

KATE   Never mind that now. Why did you do it? What on
earth possessed you?

MAUREEN   My fella's back in Belfast, he's been away for a
month. I was goin' to see him the night. I wanted to
look nice.

KATE   Why didn't you ask me? I could have lent you
something to wear.

MAUREEN   I wanted somethin' new. My own. I'm fed up
wearin' other people's cast-offs . . . I didn't go in
to do nuthin' . . . I only went in to look . . . I've
been eyin' that suit fer months . . . I heard they
was all reduced . . . I only went in to see . . . I
was standin' there, trying' to make up my mind . . .
the jacket was still too dear, but I had enough saved
for the skirt or the trousers . . . I thought maybe
the skirt . . . he said I had nice legs . . . an' then
this woman an' her daughter come up, an' the girl
tried on one of the jackets . . . an' it was lovely on
her so it was . . . an' she said . . . she said, 'Do
ye think I should get the trousers or the skirt' an'
the woman said, 'Get both, it's not every day you're
seventeen . . . ' I followed them roun' the shop
. . . they bought matchin' shoes an' a top . . . the
shoes were real leather, reduced til twelve pounds
. . . everything she was wearin' was brand new.
What did she need with more clothes? Her mother
bought her the lot . . . wrote a cheque . . . I just
walked behind them . . . watchin' . . . an' then
they stopped at the blouses . . . they set the bag
on the floor while they were lookin' . . . an' I just

lifted it . . . an' I run . . . it's not even my size.

KATE Oh Maureen, Maureen . . .

MAUREEN They'll lock me up an' put Johnnie away, an it'll all be my fault . . .

KATE I'll phone a solicitor, ask him to go to the station . . .

MAUREEN I'm sorry . . . I don't know why I done it . . . it was wrong . . .

KATE It's all wrong, and none of it is your fault, so stop apologising.

MAUREEN I've let ye down, I'm sorry . . .

KATE No, I've let you down . . . you know what my reaction was when the police told me? How could Maureen do this to me . . . my star pupil . . . I'm becoming more and more like them . . . expecting you to be grateful for nothing. Sandra's right. I might as well live on the moon for all I know. Everything I have taken for granted all my life, you have had to fight for. Ordinary things like a warm dry house, nice clothes, education, opportunity, choice. You have no choice. None of you have. Poverty on the dole, or poverty on a Youth Opportunities Programme. And if you're very good and aspire to be like us, we might even find you a job.

MAUREEN I've no chance of gettin' a job in an office now, have I? Not with a police record.

KATE Maureen, you are going to have to learn how to fight, or they'll destroy you . . . I'll phone for a solicitor.

KATE *goes to the phone. As she dials there are noises, shouts from the street outside.* TOMMY *rushes in.*

TOMMY Maureen! It's your Johnnie! He's nicked the fuckin' police car. He's coked to the gills, ridin' it round and round the block. The army's in the next street. Somebody'd better stop him before they do . . .

MAUREEN No!

She runs out. KATE *runs after her.* ARTHUR *comes in. He is nervous, agitated.*

TOMMY   It's Johnnie.

ARTHUR   I know. I seen him.

They look out of the window.

TOMMY   (*admiringly*): Jeesus, look at him. He's like the friggin' 'A' Team . . . go on ye wee bugger. You show them . . .

There is a rattle of gunfire, screams, shouts.

TOMMY   Jeesus Christ!

ARTHUR *turns away from the window, puts his hands on his head, walks abruptly to the kitchen. He lifts a lettuce, pulls it apart. He is shaking.*

TOMMY   What are ye doin'?

ARTHUR   Shreddin' lettuce . . . you shouldn't cut it ye know . . . it destroys the vitamin C content if ye use a knife.

He is very agitated. His head hurts as he tries to block the memory of being shot and the subsequent slow, painful recovery.

TOMMY   Arthur?

ARTHUR   There is no pain ye know . . . not when yer hurt that bad . . . the brain shuts down . . . it's what saves ye . . . the oul brain knows when you've had enough . . . when it's more than a body can take . . . an' it shuts down . . . that way ye don't die of shock . . . you know what the worst bit is? . . . when ye sort of come to . . . an' ye can hear, but ye can't see an' ye can't speak . . . I remember I was scared they might think I was dead an' bury me alive . . . I thought I'd go mad . . . I thought maybe I *was* dead . . . but I wasn't . . . I wasn't. You can be shot to bits an' not be dead . . .

TOMMY   Arthur . . . Arthur!

ARTHUR   What's happenin' out there?

TOMMY *looks out of the window again.*

TOMMY   The street's fulla kids, dozens of them. They're all over the place, screamin' shoutin' throwin' stones at the army and the police . . . the kids won't let them near the car . . . an' yer man Saunders has arrived, an' the Brits are tryin' to protect him, get his big Mercedes out the street . . . it's like bedlam out there . . . I can't see . . .

SANDRA comes in. She is carrying MAUREEN. MAUREEN *is a horrific bloody mess.*

SANDRA (*quietly, without expression*): Lock the door.

TOMMY locks the door. SANDRA *sets* MAUREEN *on the chair below the hairdryer.* MAUREEN *sprawls grotesquely, half on the chair, half on the floor.*

SANDRA (*expressionlessly*): She run between the car an' the army.

ARTHUR I know. We seen her.

There is a brief moment when he might offer SANDRA *comfort, when she might accept. Then* SANDRA *turns away, grabs hold of* MAUREEN *shakes her, screams.*

SANDRA Ye stupid bitch, ye daft stupid bitch! Ye haven't the sense ye were born with!

ARTHUR Sandra . . .

SANDRA What are you lookin' at, face-ache!

ARTHUR She's dead, Sandra.

SANDRA I know she's friggin' dead. Her guts is everywhere. That's what dying's like. (*She shakes* MAUREEN.) This is what it's like. Do you hear me? It's not lovely, an' it's not romantic like in stupid friggin' plays!

ARTHUR Don't, Sandra.

SANDRA Nobody's ever gonna write poetry about you! Nobody!

ARTHUR Don't. It's not right.

There is a loud hammering on the door.

SANDRA Fuck off! If you let the Brits touch her, so help me, Arthur, I'll stove in yer steel plate . . .

KATE (*offstage*): Arthur, Sandra, Tommy, please . . . open the door . . .

SANDRA	Give them a signed statement. Tell them she done it for love.
KATE	Please let me in.
ARTHUR	Ye just can't keep her here, Sandra.
SANDRA	Why not? Nobody else wants her.
ARTHUR	Let Kate in, Tommy.
KATE	Please, open the door.
TOMMY	Are ye on yer own Kate?
	Sounds of argument outside.
KATE	Yes.
TOMMY	Swear.
KATE	I swear. Please, let me in.
	TOMMY *opens the door.* KATE *comes in.* TOMMY *locks the door again.* KATE *looks at* MAUREEN. *Looks away.*
KATE	Move her out of that chair.
SANDRA	Put her back on the knittin' machine.
	ARTHUR *pushes the food and the glasses off the table on to the floor. Lifts* MAUREEN. *Lays her gently on the table.*
KATE	Cover her with something.
SANDRA	Look at her. Everybody should look at her.
TOMMY	Did they get Johnnie as well?
KATE	He got a few cuts from the windscreen, that's all.
TOMMY	Jammy wee bugger. He always did have the luck of the devil.
	Hammering on the door.
SANDRA	Do you know what it'll say in the papers the morra? 'Shoplifter gets shot.'
	Blackout.
	In the darkness SANDRA *sings quietly* 'Wouldn't It Be Good To Be In Your Shoes Even If It Was For Just One Day'. MAUREEN *is carried off stage by* ARTHUR. TOMMY *chants* 'No Job Nothin' To Do, No Money, On

The Bru'. SANDRA *sings quietly* 'We Are the Divis
Girls We Wear Our Hair In Curls'.

KATE *sings* 'Damp, Damp, Damp, Damp, Damp,
Damp, Damp, Damp'.

ARTHUR *returns singing* 'As I Was Out Walkin'
Outside Divis Flats, Where the Happiest Tenants Are
Surely the Rats'.

In semi-darkness, KATE, ARTHUR, SANDRA *and* TOMMY
*clear the stage, singing excerpts of the songs from the
play, which merge into a distorted medley.*

Rats, rats, rats, rats, rats, rats, rats, rats.
What will it be when we leave school.
Will it be Ace schemes or Y.T.P.
No job after school. No future that's the rule.

Unemployment. Unemployment.

Hope it's work real work
We hope it's work real work
We hope it's work real work
And not the dole.

Old Mother Hubbard went to the cupboard
To get a piece of bread
She put her hand in the breadbin
And found something else instead
AUGH!

SANDRA *sings loudly, defiantly*

We are the Divis girls we wear our hair in curls
We wear our skinners to our knees
We do not smoke or drink
That's what our parents think
We are the Divis girls
We are the Divis Street crowd of rowdies
We are a nuisance to the public I agree
I agree!
See us stand and talk to each other
We are mates, we are great, we agree.

KATE, ARTHUR *and* TOMMY *exit.* SANDRA *sits down on a
chair, lights a cigarette.*

OR *alternatively:*

After SANDRA'S *line* ' . . . Shoplifter gets shot'

Blackout

MAUREEN *is carried off stage and there is no singing, only the sound of broken glass being swept up. (This is the sound that usually follows violence in Belfast.)*

Scene Four

Early May. The Belfast Arts Council Gallery. SANDRA *sitting smoking a cigarette.* ARTHUR *comes in. He is wearing the 'Compensation Day' suit casually (sleeves rolled back and an expensive T-shirt.) Already he looks more prosperous, more middle class.*

ARTHUR   What's the use of comin' til an art exhibition if ye don't look at the pictures.

SANDRA   I have looked at the pictures. They're a load of crap.

ARTHUR   The man what done them is downstairs. He's from Russia.

SANDRA   If he was from roun' here, nobody'd give them a second look. I've seen better at the primary school open day.

ARTHUR   Kate says people are payin' hundreds for them.

SANDRA   Why don't ye put in an offer fer one. You'll be gettin' yer money any day now, won't ye?

ARTHUR   I have it all earmarked.

SANDRA   You treatin' yerself till a brain transplant?

ARTHUR   I'm takin' over Larry's.

SANDRA   Yer what?

ARTHUR   I've made him an offer he can't refuse. I'm gonna do it all up. Serve good food.

SANDRA   Did they pack yer head with green cheese in the hospital? Ye'll go broke in a year.

ARTHUR   I'm gonna have candles on the tables an' a man playin' the accordion.

SANDRA   I'll take you home again, Kathleen.

ARTHUR   Real French stuff. Ye hafta get them in the mood.

SANDRA   They'll set fire til the tableclothes with the candles.

ARTHUR   Not if you were there.

SANDRA   Me?

ARTHUR   The family's gonna help me out, part time, till I get goin' . . . but I need somebody full time . . . a supervisor . . . to keep an eye on the place while I'm doin' the cookin' . . . make sure my da keeps his hands outa the till.

SANDRA   What makes ye think I would keep my hands outa yer till?

ARTHUR   No point in robbin' a business if yer a partner . . .

SANDRA   A what?

ARTHUR   I mean proper . . . one of the family.

There is an awkward, embarrassed pause.

SANDRA   Arthur . . . will you just go away an' leave me alone. Yer wearin' me out.

ARTHUR   Suit yourself.

He walks away. SANDRA *sits for a moment.*

SANDRA   The one an' only time I ever wore a white lace frock Arthur, was for my first communion . . . an' my mother parades me down the road to get my photo tuk, an' she says to the photographer, 'Isn't our Sandra a picture? Won't she make a beautiful bride?' an' I told her I was never gonna get married, an' she got all dewy-eyed because she thought I wanted to be a nun . . . A bride of Christ, or forty years' hard labour . . . my mother thinks anything in between is a mortal sin . . . She married a big child like you, Arthur, an' what did it get her . . . eight kids an' twenty years' cookin' cleanin' an' survivin' on grants an' handouts . . . You're too like my da fer comfort. Fulla big plans that'll come to nuthin' because yer too soft an' yer too easy-goin' an' havin' all that money won't make ye any

different. Whatever your da an' the rest of your ones
don't steal from ye, the world will. They'll ate ye
alive . . . You know what the big trick in this life
is? It's knowing' what ye don't want, an' I don't
want to be a back-seat joyrider, content to sit and
giggle behind the fellas who do the stealin' an' the
drivin' . . . I stole a car once . . . all by myself
. . . I never told nobody, doin' it was enough . . .
I just drove it roun' them posh streets in South
Belfast until it ran outa petrol, an' then I walked
home. Didn't need to boast about it the way the
fellas do . . . just doin' it was enough . . . When
the careers' officer come til our school, he asked me
what I wanted to do, an' I says, 'I wanna drive roun'
in a big car like yer woman outa Bonnie an' Clyde,
an' rob banks,' an' he thought I was takin' a hand
out him, so I says, 'All right then, I'll settle fer bein'
a racin' driver.' An' he says, 'I'd advise you to settle
for something less fantastic Sandra.' . . . They're all
the same. They ask ye what ye wanta be, an' then
they tell ye what yer allowed to be . . . Me wantin'
to be a racin' driver is no more fantastical than
Maureen believin' the fairy stories . . . dilly day-
dream, just like her mother before her . . .
somewhere over the rainbow, bluebirds die . . .

KATE *comes in.*

KATE   You know the best thing about this exhibition?

SANDRA   What?

KATE   The free wine.

SANDRA   Somebody's payin' for it. Nuthin's free.

KATE   Tommy's right. You should join the Party.

SANDRA   I went to visit Tommy on the way here.

KATE   How is he?

SANDRA   His left hand's okay. The right hand . . . they're
gonna hafta break it an' reset some of the bones.

KATE   Oh God.

SANDRA   Lucky he's left handed . . . born klut
         half-caste. God gave him a good start i.
         he . . . Did you get to read the report .
         done on Maureen.

KATE   Yes.

SANDRA   What did it say?

KATE   It said that she died of gunshot wounds.

SANDRA   Did it say anything else about her?

         KATE *pauses. They look at each other for a moment.*

KATE   Why didn't she tell me . . . Why didn't you tell me?

SANDRA   I thought maybe she imagined it. She was forever
         day-dreamin' . . . Have you ever been to the
         Botanic Gardens, Kate?

KATE   Yes. It's really lovely. As well as the park, there's a
         palm house and a tropical ravine, and the Ulster
         Museum . . . Would you like to go sometime?

SANDRA   No.

         *The lights dim to sound of Nik Kershaw's recording
         of 'Wouldn't It Be Good To Be In Your Shoes.'*

Did You Hear The One About The Irishman . . . ?

for Richard Howard

Details of First Performance

Did You Hear the One About the Irishman . . . ? was first performed by the Royal Shakespeare Company on tour in America in 1985. This updated version was produced at the Kings Head Theatre, London in 1987 with the following cast:

ALLISON CLARKE	Janet Behan
BRIAN RAFFERTY	John Keegan
THE COMEDIAN	Richard Howard
MRS BOYD ⎫	
MRS CLARKE ⎬	Jane Lowe
BERNIE CASSIDY ⎭	
MR CLARKE ⎫	Ultan Ely O'Carroll
THE IRISHMAN/NEWSREADER ⎭	
HUGHIE BOYD ⎫	Billy Clarke
JOE RAFFERTY ⎭	
MARIE RAFFETY	Mandy McIlwaine

Director	Caroline Sharman
Designer	Angus Campbell
Lighting Design	Steve O'Brien
Stage Manager	Mark Jones
Production Assistant	Lauren Emmerson

Belfast 1987

IRISHMAN   (*reading from a list*): Her Majesty's Prison, Maze, Lisburn, Northern Ireland, 1987. Permitted Christmas Parcels for H blocks. 25 small cigars (cigarette size) or 100 cigarettes or 4 and half oz. tobacco.

2lb chocolates or sweets. 2lb cake quartered. 2lb loose biscuits.
One unstuffed chicken, boned and quartered.
1lb sliced cooked meat.
4lb Fresh Fruit – No bananas or pears.

Spotlight on the COMEDIAN. *He tells jokes directly to the audience as if he is performing in a club. The* IRISHMAN *stops reading the list as his voice is drowned by the* COMEDIAN'S *voice. He watches the comedy routine impassively.*

COMEDIAN   Good morning everyone. This is your captain speaking. We are now approaching the city of Belfast. Will all passengers please fasten their seatbelts and turn their watches back three hundred years.

The time is seven a.m. And if there are any Irish passengers on board, that means that the big hand is at twelve and the little hand is at seven.

Did you hear the one about the Irishman whose plane ran out of peat? He radioed for help. Mayday! Mayday!

'Cleared to land', answered Control, 'Can you give us your height and position?'

'Certainly', said the Irishman, 'I'm five foot two and I'm sitting at the front of the plane.' Then there was the Irish terrorist whose first assignment was to hijack an aeroplane. It turned out to be his last assignment. As soon as the plane took off he lit the fuse, put the bomb under his seat, and told the

captain that everybody had three minutes to get out.
Little Paddy heard the story and it made him very
nervous about flying. So he always carried a bomb
in his suitcase every time he had to travel by plane.
He figured that the chances of two people on the
same flight carrying a bomb were practically nil.

The COMEDIAN *pauses to drink some beer.*

IRISHMAN   Individual Christmas parcels. Maze Prison.
Compound 17. 400 Cigarettes or 12 oz. tobacco or
25 small cigars.

6 mince pies.
One fruit loaf – 1lb.
6 Pastries.
6 Baps.
1lb Chocolates.
2lb Sweets.
3lb Christmas Cake with no marzipan.

The Rafferty House. 7a.m.

BRIAN RAFFERTY *and his sister* MARIE *are packing a
food parcel for their brother* JOE *who is in the Maze
Prison.*

BRIAN   You know, a committee of grown men must have
sat round a table and compiled these lists and
decided that marzipan was a threat to national
security.

MARIE   Where are you going?

BRIAN   I'm going to phone Allison.

MARIE   You'll finish this first!

BRIAN   I'll finish it when I've phone Allison.

He goes to the phone.

MARIE   She'll be the finish of you, that one.

COMEDIAN   An Irish telephonist answered an international call.
It's a long distance from America, said the operator.
Sure any fool knows that, said the Irish telephonist,
and hung up.

IRISHMAN   Bulk Christmas Parcels. Maze Prison. Compound 17.
                 2 large tins of coffee.
                 5 turkeys cooked and stuffed.
                 8lb sausages, cooked.
                 2 mince pies per prisoner.
                 2 pastries per prisoner – small bun size.
                 8 cakes not over 2lb. each.
                 12 christmas puddings not over 2lb. each.
                 3 christmas trees maximum 4ft. 6 inches.
                 No decorations. Prisoners to buy them from the
                 tuck shop. All parcels to be signed.

COMEDIAN   (*to the* IRISHMAN): Have you heard the latest Irish
                 joke?

IRISHMAN   I'm warning you. I'm an Irishman myself.

COMEDIAN   That's all right Paddy. I'll tell it nice and slowly for
                 you.

                 The Clarke House 7a.m.

                 ALLISON *sitting waiting for* BRIAN *to call. The phone
                 rings. She smiles and lifts the receiver.*

BRIAN   It's 7am and this is your early morning obscene
                 telephone call. You have three minutes to get
                 aroused.

                 MRS CLARKE, ALLISON'S *mother, enters.*

ALLISON   I'm sorry caller. Security are here to check the
                 bugging device. Please call later. (*She replaces the
                 receiver.*) Good morning Mother.

MRS CLARKE   Who was that on the phone?

ALLISON   (*smiling*): The Divis Flats heavy breather.

MRS CLARKE   Oh really Allison. Can't you be serious about
                 anything!

ALLISON   You know very well who it was, mother. And yes,
                 I'm serious about a lot of things, but you don't
                 want to know about them. Particularly at seven
                 o'clock on a Saturday morning. What are you
                 doing out of bed this early anyway? Is there a
                 bomb scare in our select suburb?

MRS CLARKE   That's not funny, Allison.

ALLISON   No, it's not.

MRS CLARKE   Susan phoned last night when you were out. She left you a message.

ALLISON   She's emigrating.

MRS CLARKE   I do wish you two could be friends.

ALLISON   Mother, it is a legal fact that when Susan married your beloved son, I acquired a sister in law. There is no law says I have to like her.

MRS CLARKE   She's such a lovely, likeable girl. A good wife and mother. A considerate daughter-in-law.

ALLISON   A lousy daughter.

MRS CLARKE   Susan is very generous to her own mother.

ALLISON   Then this message is not what I suspect it is?

MRS CLARKE   Susan can't take Mrs Boyd to . . . that place . . . today.

ALLISON   That place is called Long Kesh. The Maze Prison. And Susan's brother Hughie is one of its most notorious inmates. What's today's excuse for not giving her mother a lift there in the nice new car you bought her for Christmas?

MRS CLARKE   Susan has a cold.

ALLISON   In her feet no doubt.

MRS CLARKE   She wanted to know if you would give Mrs Boyd a lift, as it's your morning for voluntary work.

ALLISON   Voluntary work? Is that what you tell your friends I do at the camp.

MRS CLARKE   Well, it is what you do.

ALLISON   I make tea.

MRS CLARKE   Well, there you are then.

ALLISON   It's not like the Women's Institute, mother. It's a drafty hut where the relatives of the prisoners hang around waiting for security clearance before they're bused up the road to the main camp. Voluntary work! Do you know what Susan calls it?

Doing my middle class bit. Mingling with the lower orders, the undeserving poor, from behind the safety of a tea urn on a counter. And she's right. That's what galls me. In her own nasty little way, she's right. But she has no right to judge me. Her only brother has been remanded there for over a year, and she has been to see him once.

MRS CLARKE She doesn't know what to say to Hughie.

ALLISON No. She's married into the middle classes; got herself out of those mean back streets; and his arrest has forced her to look back to what she came from.

MRS CLARKE She is not responsible for her brother.

ALLISON She could care a little more about her mother.

MRS CLARKE You're very hard on poor Susan. I think she's coped wonderfully well under the circumstances. It hasn't been easy for her.

ALLISON It hasn't been easy for her mother either. Have you any idea what it's like for a quiet, gentle little woman like Mrs Boyd to go to that place alone. To face the searches, the questions, the police guard while you try to talk to your only son?

The phone rings again. ALLISON *lifts the receiver.*

BRIAN I've thought it over, and I've decided to give you a second chance.

ALLISON To do what?

BRIAN To tell me how madly you love me.

ALLISON Love you? Are you mad? You're a working class Catholic.

BRIAN I'm a very sexy working class Catholic.

ALLISON Are you going to make an honest woman of me?

BRIAN Not until you've told me why you hung up on me.

ALLISON I got distracted by a message from your cousin, the lovely Susan.

BRIAN   Ah, let me guess . . . She's broken her leg and can't drive to Long Kesh today.

ALLISON   Congratulations contestant. You have won first prize in our 'spot-the-lame-excuse' competition.

BRIAN   No stamina, these middle class prods.

ALLISON   Common Catholics are not permitted to speak ill of the Protestant Ascendancy. It's written into The Constitution.

BRIAN   I didn't know that.

ALLISON   It's in the small print. Now, if I were your wife, I couldn't be called to give evidence against you.

BRIAN   If you were my wife, I'd be part of the Protestant Ascendancy.

ALLISON   Well, if you don't want to become a handsome prince, I'll become a frog. I'm not proud.

BRIAN   You never give up, do you.

ALLISON   Never.

BRIAN   If I let you take me out tonight and get me drunk, will you promise not to take advantage of me.

ALLISON   No.

BRIAN   Nine o'clock?

ALLISON   Nine o'clock.

BRIAN   And will you drive Aunt Isa to the camp to see Hughie?

ALLISON   You know I will.

BRIAN   You know, you're not a bad sort . . . for a Protestant.

ALLISON   I love you.

BRIAN   I know.

ALLISON *replaces the receiver.*

MRS CLARKE   Allison . . .

ALLISON   Not now mother. I have to pick up Mrs Boyd and be at the camp by nine.

MRS CLARKE   We have got to have a serious talk sometime soon.

ALLISON   Mother, I am over eighteen and I don't need your permission to do anything.

MRS CLARKE   You're not serious about this person, are you?

ALLISON   He has a name, mother. Brian Rafferty. He was here only last week. Remember? Eye-patch. Wooden leg. Parrot on his shoulder.

MRS CLARKE   He is most unsuitable.

ALLISON   Why?

MRS CLARKE   His background . . .

ALLISON   Is exactly the same as Susan's.

MRS CLARKE   His family . . .

ALLISON   Is Catholic, and Susan's is not.

MRS CLARKE   His brother is a terrorist.

ALLISON   So is Susan's. Or are there terrorists and terrorists, mother? Theirs and ours?

MRS CLARKE   Henry is very concerned about this whole affair.

ALLISON   You are not to discuss my affairs with Uncle Henry.

MRS CLARKE   A marriage of this sort could have a detrimental effect on your Uncle Henry's career.

ALLISON   Mother, if I thought for one moment that me marrying a Catholic could put a stop to Uncle Henry's career, as you call it, I'd marry the first Catholic who'd have me.

MRS CLARKE   My brother is a very important man.

ALLISON   Your brother is a well-bred gangster.

MRS CLARKE   He says he will not permit this.

ALLISON   How's he planning to stop us?

MRS CLARKE *looks uncomfortable and moves away.*

ALLISON   Mother! What did he say!

The Rafferty House.

BRIAN *returns to help* MARIE *pack* JOE'S *parcel.*

MARIE   And how is little miss wonderful this morning?

Nobody's put a bullet through her head yet, I take it?

BRIAN   Marie, some day that mouth of yours is going to get your nose broke.

MARIE   Or better still, maybe somebody'll put a bullet through her Uncle Henry's head.

BRIAN   Stop it, Marie.

MARIE   I don't understand how you can go about with the likes of her. It's her kind are responsible for our Joe being where he is. You should be concentrating on getting him out of that place. Not knocking about with well to do Prods. from up the Malone Road.

BRIAN   I'm sorry to be such a disappointment to you and your friends, Marie. I tell you what. As soon as I get my Rambo Outfit back from the cleaners, I'll scale the wire and carry our Joe out on my back.

MARIE   Long Kesh is no joking matter.

BRIAN   No it's not. (*Pause.*) Wouldn't it be a laugh though, if that camp was what united the Irish, once and for all.

MARIE   What are you blethering on about now.

BRIAN   Where else do you know of in Northern Ireland where the Prods. and the Fenians meet on common ground?

MARIE   Let's all say a wee prayer together? Our church this week, their church next week?

BRIAN   I said Prods. and Fenians, Marie. Not well-meaning moderates.

MARIE   The camp, like the country, is segregated.

BRIAN   I'm not talking about the prisoners. I'm talking about their families. Drinking tea in the waiting area. Together. Standing in line checking in food parcels. Together. Sharing the same bus to the main camp to visit their sons, fathers, husbands, brothers, lovers. Together.

MARIE   They don't visit together. They go their separate

ways to segregated blocks. Prods to the right.
Fenians to the left.

BRIAN But before that they've sat together and talked.
Without fighting. Which is more than can be said
about their so-called political leaders. Maybe we
should put all the Politicians on the Long Kesh bus,
and drive them round and round the camp till
they've reached an agreement.

MARIE There'll be no agreement here as long as there are
H Blocks and men on the blanket.

BRIAN There are Protestants in the prison as well, Marie.

MARIE One or two.

BRIAN Well the pair of them must have a hell of a lot of
visitors, that's all I can say.

MARIE All right. All right. So there are Protestants in jail
too. So what!

BRIAN So, where else in Northern Ireland can a Provie
wife and a U.D.A. wife take a long look at each
other and realise that they're both on board the
same sinking ship. Common ground. Common
Enemy. And there's nothing like a common enemy
for resolving a family feud.

MARIE It's too late Brian.

BRIAN It's never too late to hold out your hand.

MARIE You're a dreamer. They'd tie your hands behind
your back and shoot you. You finish Joe's box. I'll
take mum up a cup of tea.

BRIAN How is she the day?

MARIE Same as usual. Full of life and hope. Chatting away,
ten to the dozen.

BRIAN Don't, Marie.

MARIE What do you want me to say! You know how she
is! You still believe there'll be a miraculous cure
don't you. That some morning she won't be lying
in that bed staring blankly at the cracks in the
ceiling. How is she the day! She's the same as she's

been every day since some Protestant hero crept up behind daddy and fired a bullet into the back of his head.

BRIAN   We don't know who killed him, Marie.

MARIE   Maybe he shot himself.

The Clarke House.

ALLISON'S *father,* MR CLARKE *comes in.*

MR CLARKE   What are you doing up at this hour on a Saturday morning?

ALLISON   It's my Saturday for making tea at the Maze. What's your excuse?

MR CLARKE   Didn't your mother tell you? We're going to Enniskillen for the weekend. Your Uncle Henry is having one of his do's.

ALLISON   Oh daddy. Why don't you just refuse to go.

MR CLARKE   Your mother would sulk for a fortnight. Besides, I like to keep on friendly terms with Henry. If we ever get our parliament back, he could be our new leader.

ALLISON   God forbid.

MR CLARKE   He was born with the gift of the gab.

ALLISON   I wonder how many people have died as a result of his clever speeches.

MR CLARKE   What's the matter, love?

ALLISON   It's been one of those mornings. Susan's leaving her mother to face the camp alone again. And mother's been going on about Brian. How unsuitable he is, wrong class, wrong religion . . . do you disapprove of Brian?

MR CLARKE   If I let you into a family secret will you promise never to tell your mother that I told you? My grandmother was Catholic. A native Irish speaker from Donegal. I think your mother is very worried that it might be a hereditary complaint coming out in you.

ALLISON   Dad, I get enough jokes from Brian. Don't you start.

MR CLARKE   No joke love. Just the unspoken truth. It was an important clause in the marriage contract that it should never be mentioned. I think over the years, your mother has convinced herself that my grandmother was a senile old woman who only imagined she was born a Catholic.

ALLISON   You wouldn't object then, if I married Brian?

MR CLARKE   You're over eighteen.

ALLISON   That's not an answer.

MR CLARKE   It would . . . worry me.

ALLISON   Why?

MR CLARKE   I don't care one way or the other about religion. You know that. I'm all for people leaving each other alone. But unfortunately, there are too many people here who do care. I don't want to see you getting hurt.

ALLISON   Bigoted opinions don't bother me.

MR CLARKE   It's not what they'd say, Allison. It's what they might do.

ALLISON   Oh come on daddy. Brian and I aren't that important.

MR CLARKE   Whether you like it or not, you are the niece of a loyalist politician. You marry a Catholic and it will be headline news. Especially when word gets out that the groom's brother is Joe Rafferty.

ALLISON   You do disapprove.

MR CLARKE   No. I like Brian. He's witty, articulate, good education, good job. In any other time and place the perfect son-in-law. But not here Allison, not now.

ALLISON   I was prepared for objections from every side. His family. Mother's family. All comers. But not you. Not my nice easy-going, middle of-the-road dad.

MR CLARKE   Listen to me love.

ALLISON   Don't waste your breath trying to talk me out of it.

MR CLARKE   Let me tell you another family story from way back. Your grandfather, my father, had a stroke and I found myself suddenly in charge of the factory. There was . . . an arrangement . . . about the workforce. There wasn't a Catholic employed in the place. Protestants all. From the managing director to the old man who swept the floors. I'd always known about it, but I'd never really given it much thought until I became the boss. I'd been away from Ireland a lot. Educated in England. Travels abroad. I considered myself a liberal thinker. I was naive enough to believe that good intentions would change the world. Your Brian is like that. I was wrong, of course. When word got around the factory that I'd shortlisted a Catholic woman for canteen manageress, I received a delegation from the men. The message was very clear. Don't even consider it or we shut down the plant. The same day, I was summoned to my father's bedside. He was propped up with pillows. Half paralysed. But *his* message was also very clear. One more stunt like that and he'd bring my cousin George in as head of the family business. Whatever damn fool ideas I'd picked up in Oxford, I could forget them.

ALLISON   So you forgot them.

MR CLARKE   I'd like to claim a great crisis of conscience. But I'm afraid I can't. I was an indolent young man. I had a sports car. An expensive social life, here and abroad. All paid for by my father's factory with his loyal Protestant workforce. I wasn't about to rock that gilt-edged boat for lost causes.

ALLISON   You've never deliberately harmed anyone. Not like Uncle Henry.

MR CLARKE   I've never gone out of my way to help anyone either. What is happening now in this country has come about not just because of greedy politicians, but because of people like me. Influential people of my generation who knew it was wrong, but did nothing to change it. The sins of the fathers shall be visited on the children. As my father was threatening me in his sick slurred voice, the face of his beautiful Catholic mother was smiling down at us from over the fireplace in his bedroom. He loved her. But when she was dying and asked for a Priest, in Irish, he pretended not to understand what she was saying. Perhaps the child of a mixed marriage has more to prove than most.

ALLISON Is that what's worrying you? My children?

MR CLARKE What's really worrying me is that you might not live long enough to have any children.

Pause.

ALLISON I'm going to marry him.

MR CLARKE When?

ALLISON As soon as he'll have me. He keeps turning me down you see. Says he can't afford to keep me in the style to which I am accustomed.

The Rafferty house.

Sounds of coughing offstage. BRIAN *grins as* BERNIE CASSIDY *enters.*

BRIAN Morning Bernie. You're coughing better. I thought the doctor said you were to give up the fegs.

BERNIE Ach bugger him. You're a long time dead. Have you any spare seats in the mini-bus the day?

BRIAN I thought your Peter got out last week?

BERNIE Oh he did. But I'm takin' a parcel down for young Declan Reilly. His mother's in bed with her stomach again.

BRIAN I think you like going down to The Maze, Bernie.

BERNIE When you've been goin' down twice a week for two years, it's hard to give up. Like the fegs.

BRIAN And how's your Peter coping with the big wide world?

BERNIE Oh he's alright. I'm the one that's sufferin'.

BRIAN Ah now, two years is a long time Mrs Cassidy. They say it can make an animal of a man.

BERNIE You're an awful wee boy Brian. I'm not talkin' about that. Jeesus, I wish I was.

BRIAN Well, what are you talking about then?

BERNIE Well to tell you the truth Brian, I never had such a good time in all my married life as I did when he got lifted. 'Ach Mrs Cassidy, sorry to hear about your wee bit of trouble. Can I get you a drink?' Jeesus it was stickin' out, while it lasted. But you see now he's out? My tongue could be hangin' out to my knees for all the notice anybody takes of me. Nobody's bought me as much as a packet of crisps in the last fortnight. You see when your man's put away? You're a star. You see when he gets out? You're nuthin'.

MARIE *enters.*

MARIE Everybody's in the mini-bus, ready to go.
Hello Bernie.

BERNIE Hello Marie, love.

BRIAN Well, I'd better get my driving gloves on, for the mystery tour.

BERNIE Any prizes for guessin' where we're going?

BRIAN First prize, one week in Long Kesh. Second prize?

BERNIE Two weeks in Long Kesh.

BRIAN Third prize, indefinite internment.

BERNIE God, you're a tonic Brian. Here, these fegs'll never see me through the day. Hang on. I'll not be a minute. Don't be goin' without me now.

BERNIE *rushes out. There is a slight pause.*

MARIE Brian . . . I'm sorry about this morning. I just get angry. Every morning I go into her room and I think, this is the day it's going to be all right. She's going to be back to normal. Sitting up. Smiling. But she never is.

BRIAN   Allison's not responsible for what happened to
              mum.

MARIE   I said I'm sorry.

BRIAN   You know, when you take off your black beret and
              dark glasses and stop mouthing political slogans,
              you're not a bad looking girl at all. If you weren't
              my sister, I'd ask you out.

MARIE   Are you ever serious about anything?

BRIAN   Only the increasing shortage of good pubs since
              the bombing started.

              Spotlight on the COMEDIAN.

COMEDIAN Did you hear about the Irishman who was arrested
              for shoplifting? He lifted the shop three feet off the
              ground. What happened to the Irishman who tried
              to blow up a bus? He burned his lips on the
              exhaust pipe.
              A Belfast businessman rushed into an insurance
              office and asked. 'How much to insure my car
              against fire?' 'Thirty pounds sir', said the clerk, 'but
              for only ten pounds extra you can insure it against
              theft as well.'
              'Don't talk daft', said the businessman, 'Sure, who'd
              want to steal a burning car.'

IRISHMAN Clothing permitted for remand prisoners.
              1 pair of shoes. Trainers are allowed but no shoes
              with steel tips.
              3 pairs of socks. 3 sets of underwear.
              3 pair of trousers – jeans accepted. 3 shirts.
              No pure white, black, blue or green colours are
              allowed for any article of clothing.

COMEDIAN What do you do if an Irishman throws a pin at you?
              Run like hell. He's probably got a grenade between
              his teeth.
              Did you hear the one about the Irishman whose
              library was burned down? Both books were
              destroyed. And worse still, one of them hadn't even
              been coloured in.

Belfast City Hall was bombed and the Lord Mayor phoned the Fire Brigade. 'Have you taken any steps to quench the blaze?' asked the fire chief. 'My staff are pouring buckets of water on it' said the Lord Mayor.

'Well, there's no point in us coming over', said the fire chief, 'sure that's all we'd be doing too.'

IRISHMAN   2 pairs of pyjamas. Only type with elastic waistbands are acceptable.

3 jumpers. No slogans allowed except manufacturer's trade mark – for example, Adidas.

COMEDIAN   Mick and Paddy were planting a bomb, and Mick said, 'Hey Paddy, hold that wire'. And then Mick put his fingers in his ears. A couple of minutes later he took them out again and said, 'What happened?' 'Nothing', said Paddy. 'Thank God for that', said Mick, 'it must be the other wire that triggers the explosion'. He must be the same Irishman who read a poster that said: Man wanted for bombing and murder. So he went in and applied for the job.

What's the fastest sport in the world? Pass the parcel in an Irish pub.

An Irish pub was bombed and the landlord rushed to the nearest telephone box. 'Hello, is that 999?' 'No, this is 998'. 'Well, would you ever nip next door and tell tham me pub's on fire?'

He was the same barman who thought that Vat 69 was the Pope's telephone number.

IRISHMAN   One outdoor jacket. Not hooded.

One indoor jacket. Not leather or imitation leather. Bomber jackets not allowed.

The Maze Prison. 9a.m.

BRIAN *and* MARIE *in the waiting room.*

ALLISON *enters with their Aunt* MRS BOYD.

BRIAN   Hello Aunt Isa.

MRS BOYD   Hello Brian love. *(Slight pause.)* Hello Marie.

MARIE *takes* JOE'S *parcel from* BRIAN.

MARIE   I'll go and sign our Joe's parcel in.

She exits. There is a small awkward silence.

BRIAN   Give me Hughie's parcel, Allison. I'll sign it in. You get the tea urn going.

ALLISON *hands him* HUGHIE'S *parcel and leaves* BRIAN *alone with* MRS BOYD.

BRIAN   I'm sorry about Marie.

MRS BOYD   She was very close to your dad.

BRIAN   We all were. Including you. He used to tease my mother, you know. Say it was a close thing whether he married her or you. (*Hurriedly, because* MRS BOYD *looks as if she might cry.*) Here, these are for Hughie. I called round with them yesterday, but you weren't in.

He puts a packet of cigarettes into HUGHIE'S *box.* ALLISON *returns.*

ALLISON   Tea'll be ready in about five minutes.

BRIAN   I'll go and check the parcel in. You haven't hidden a file or anything in the baps, have you Aunt Isa?

MRS BOYD   I'll do it, Brian.

BRIAN   No, I want to do it. Joe Rafferty's brother checking in a parcel for the Protestant compound? The computer'll do its nut.

He exits.

MRS BOYD   He's a good boy. Always was. I remember him when he was a little child. Always laughing.

ALLISON   He still is.

MRS BOYD   Are the two of you still going out together?

ALLISON   Yes. You're not going to give me a lecture, are you? I get enough of those from my mother.

MRS BOYD   Do you go to his house?

ALLISON   Not very often.

MRS BOYD   We used to go there every Sunday for our tea. Me and Hughie and Susan. After my Sammy died. It all seems such a long time ago.

ALLISON   Why don't you go and see her. She just lies in her bed, day in day out, staring, seeing God knows what.

MRS BOYD   I remember the day she married Paddy Rafferty. Lovely she was. Dark blue suit. Kid gloves. I bought her the gloves. Mother and father refused to go to the wedding. But we went. Sammy and me. My Sammy gave her away. Paddy was his mate. They were in The Union together. Thought they were going to change the world. Afterwards, in the pub, we all promised one another that no matter what happened, we'd always be close. Nothing in the world would ever drive us apart. We're twins, Molly and me. Did you know that? She was the oldest by half an hour. I used to be jealous of that when we were kids.

ALLISON   Let me take you to see her.

MRS BOYD   Then the troubles broke out, and Paddy got shot. I suppose they'd have shot my Sammy too, if the cancer hadn't got him first.

ALLISON   She might respond to you.

MRS BOYD   We went to Paddy's funeral, our Hughie and Susan and me. There was a big crowd outside in the street. A woman spat in my face. I went a few times after that. And then the threatening letters came. I was scared. There were a lot of sectarian murders that year. Anyway, our Molly didn't know me anymore. Didn't know anybody. So I stopped going. One night our Hughie got beaten up on his way from the pictures. He said Joe was there. Did nothing to help him. I couldn't believe it. Next thing I hear the police are looking for Joe in connection with an explosion in a pub in Belfast. Two people were killed. Then our Hughie took to stopping out late. By this time, Susan was married to your brother John, and the baby was on the way. I didn't want to worry her. I used to sit on my own, waiting for Hughie to come home. But when he did come back, in the small hours of the morning, I never could ask where he'd been. What he'd been doing. I suppose I knew. Didn't want to know. And now he's locked up here. And so is Joe. They were like brothers when they were kids. We used to share a house near the sea, every summer. I don't understand why all this has happened to us. Paddy and Sammy must be turning over in their graves.

ALLISON   Brian still keeps in touch with you.

MRS BOYD   Allison, I want you to tell Brian to stop visiting me. There's been talk in the street. I've tried to tell him, but he won't listen. Just laughs, makes jokes, tells me not to be so daft. I care about that wee boy like he was one of my own. I don't want to see him getting hurt.

ALLISON   Why would anyone want to hurt Brian. He's the most gentle, caring man I've ever known.

MRS BOYD   So was his father. (*Pause.*) You'd better go and help with the tea. They'll be wondering what's keeping you.

ALLISON   They've got more helpers than they need today. So, I'm going in to the camp with you to visit Hughie. Your Susan says I've no idea what it's like in there. Maybe it's about time I found out.

Spotlight on the COMEDIAN.

COMEDIAN   Of course two thirds of the Irish people don't know what the other half is doing. Maggie Thatcher was in Rome to talk to the Pope about the Northern Ireland situation, and she discovered that the Pope had a direct line to God. So she asked His Holiness if she could make the call. 'Certainly', said the Holy Father, 'but it's very expensive. About fifty million lire'. Now Maggie had used up all her traveller's cheques, so she couldn't afford to make the call. But next time she was in Belfast she noticed that

Ian Paisley *also* had a hot line to God, so she asked *him* if she could make the call.

'Certainly', said Big Ian. 'It'll cost you 10p'. '10p!' said Maggie. 'Do you know that it costs fifty million lire to phone God from the Vatican? Why is it so cheap from Belfast?' 'Because it's a local call,' said Ian.

Of course it was dear old Uncle Ian who said that all Irish people should link hands and go their separate ways.

Grow your own dope. Plant an Irishman. (*He reads from a copy of the Sun.*) Have you seen the paper today? It says here that the Irish attempt on Everest has failed. They've run out of scaffolding. Mind you, it also says that Mrs Murphy has moved her house two feet forward to take up the slack in her clothes-line. And Mr Murphy's not much better. He was given two weeks to live. So he said, 'I'll take one in June and one in September.'

Allo! The Irish daredevil Evil O'Kneivel has failed in his attempt to jump over twenty-three motor bikes in a bus.

He puts the paper aside.

What happened to the Irish jellyfish? It set! How do you tell an Irish pirate? He wears an eye-patch over both eyes.

And what about the Irish Godfather who made an offer he couldn't remember?

The Protestant compound.

ALLISON, MRS BOYD *and* HUGHIE.

MRS BOYD	There's a lovely bit of cooked ham in your parcel, son. Ellie Wilson sent it.
HUGHIE	(*To* ALLISON): Ellie Wilson nicks it out of Jamieson's shop.
MRS BOYD	She does not, Hughie.
HUGHIE	She does so. (*To* ALLISON.): Ever since oul Johnnie Jamieson refused to make a decent contribution to

the Prisoner's Defence Fund, Ellie's been feeding half the inmates here at Johnnie's expense, without him knowing it. (*Pause.*) Thanks for bringing my mother down Allison. You're more like a daughter to her than our Susan ever was.

ALLISON Brian sent you some cigarettes.

HUGHIE Allison, I have to talk to you. Now listen, and listen carefully. There's been a lot of talk in here about you and Brian. Not very nice talk.

MRS BOYD There's been talk in the street too.

HUGHIE I know. The word is that Brian's not just visiting his Aunt. That he's in our street to collect information for the other side.

ALLISON You can't believe that.

HUGHIE I've known Brian all his life. I know there's no harm in him. But they don't know that.

ALLISON Well you tell them.

HUGHIE Why should they believe me? I'm his cousin. And now they've found out that he's going about with you. They think he's a spy, sent to get information about your Uncle Henry.

ALLISON That's the daftest thing I ever heard.

HUGHIE Not half as daft as him ignoring the danger he's in. Now I can't stop him going out with you, but you're to tell him, and make sure he heeds, that he's not to visit my mother any more. Brian thinks he can joke his way out of anything. But his sense of humour won't save him if some joker decides to put a bullet through his head.

Spotlight on the COMEDIAN.

COMEDIAN Sean was confessing his sins to Father O'Reilly. 'Forgive me Father, for I have sinned. I've been to bed with a Protestant.'
'What Protestant!' roared the Priest.
'Oh, I couldn't tell you that, Father', said Sean, 'It wouldn't be honourable.'

'Was it Margaret Stewart from the fruit shop?'

'No, Father.'

'Was it that schoolteacher, Fiona Wilson?'

'No, Father.'

'Well, who was it then!'

'Forgive me, Father. But a gentleman never reveals a lady's name. Even if she is a Protestant.'

'You'll either confess her name, or do a penance of ten Hail Marys,' threatened the Priest.

'I'll do the penance Father,' said Sean, and went outside to meet his friend Paddy.

'How did you get on?' asked Paddy.

'Great,' said Sean. 'Ten Hail Marys, and a couple of dead certs for the night.'

The Catholic compound.

BRIAN, MARIE *and* JOE.

BRIAN   Allison's not really a Prod. you know. Rumour has it that her oul granda was Jewish on his mother's side.

JOE   The time for silly jokes is over, Brian. Stop seeing her. The boys don't like it.

BRIAN   The boys aren't gettin' it. Aw come on, Joe. It wasn't one of my best, but you might manage a little smile. You used to have a great sense of fun, in the old days.

JOE   The old days are over.

MARIE   Her uncle is a leading loyalist politician, committed to Protestant supremacy in The North.

BRIAN   Is that a quote from the Sein Fein Handbook, Marie? Henry Sinclair doesn't give a damn about religion. What he worships is money and power. Allison can't stand him.

JOE   We've only your word for that, Brian.

BRIAN   What's with the 'we', Joe? Do I take it, if somebody has a pot-shot at me some dark night, that you might be behind it?

JOE Don't talk stupid Brian. I'm your brother, and I've been told to tell you.

BRIAN So now you've told me.

JOE Will you stop seeing her?

BRIAN No.

JOE You don't understand.

BRIAN Oh, I understand all right.

JOE Listen to me.

BRIAN No. You listen to me. You've been here so long Joe, that you think nothing else matters but The Troubles. Well you're wrong. Outside of here, in the real world, fellas and girls still go out together. To the pubs, the parks, the pictures. Normal life goes on Joe, outside these wire fences. And that's all Allison and me are. Just a couple of normal people who fancy each other rotten . . .

JOE Listen!

BRIAN No! You listen! I'm going to marry Allison Clarke. And some cowboy threatening to blow my head off is not going to stop me.

JOE If you care about her that much, then give her up. It's not your head they're threatening to blow off. It's hers.

Spotlight on the COMEDIAN

COMEDIAN It's not widely known that God at first intended to have his Only Son born in Belfast. But he couldn't find Three Wise Men. Or a virgin.
What do you call a pregnant Irishwoman? A dope carrier.
They're all thick, the Irish. That's why it says 'Open other end' on the bottom of all the Guinness bottles.
Paddy was having a pint one night, when Mick came into the pub with a big sack over his shoulder. 'What's in the sack?' asked Paddy. 'Ducks', said Mick. Now Paddy was a bit of a punter, so he

said to Mick, 'If I guess how many ducks there are
in the sack, will you give me one of them?' 'If you
guess how many ducks there are in the bag,' said
Mick, 'I'll give you both of them.'

'Eh . . . five,' said Paddy.

Later that evening.

BRIAN *and* ALLISON *in a lounge bar in Belfast.*

BRIAN   I hate plastic pubs. And piped music.

ALLISON   Well what do you fancy? A sing-song at the U.D.A.
club? Or you could take me to a real Irish pub up
The Falls. I hear the music's great.

BRIAN   Aye, and the drink's half the price. I'm not
surprised they're so short on customers here.

ALLISON   It's early yet. The place'll fill up later.

BRIAN   It's nearly half past nine.

ALLISON   You've got your watch back.

BRIAN   One of the kids came up to me in school yesterday.
'Here's your watch, sir,' he said. 'And my big
brother says to tell you if you ever have anything
else pinched, just let him know.' How do I explain
to a nine year old boy who's never known anything
better, that I don't want his big brother threatening
to knee-cap some other little boy, if he doesn't give
the teacher back his watch? How does anybody
explain anything about law and order and
individual rights to a child whose earliest memory is
of his mother screaming when armed soldiers broke
down the door at four o'clock in the morning, and
dragged his father out of bed and into a landrover.
Why should that child respect the law that allows
the army and the police to terrorize in the name of
catching terrorists. His father was interrogated for
two days simply because he was the secretary of a
Gaelic Football team, and made regular trips across
the border to arrange matches in The South. And
after his release when he tried to sue them for

wrongful arrest, they harrassed his wife and children until he dropped the case. Now his oldest son organizes big league games for the I.R.A. and the nine year old can't wait until he's old enough to shoot a man in uniform. The British never learn, do they? Men with guns create other men with guns. And that child learned very early on that the men with the most guns win. And he's right.

ALLISON What's up doc?

BRIAN I have to have a serious talk with you, Allison.

ALLISON God, it must be the time of year. Everybody wants to talk seriously to me these days. You haven't finally made up your mind to propose to me, have you? My stars today said I would find myself in an unusual situation.

BRIAN I think maybe we should . . . ease off for a while . . . not see so much of each other . . . give ourselves time to think.

ALLISON Go on.

BRIAN I don't want to settle down. The world's full of women I've never met.

ALLISON It won't work Brian.

BRIAN Oh I don't know. If I started tomorrow, I might work my way round half of them anyway, before I'm too old to enjoy it.

ALLISON Somebody's threatened me. They have, haven't they?

BRIAN I'm not in love with you.

ALLISON Look at me when you're talking to me.

BRIAN There's a group of hard men in Long Kesh who think that you're spying for Uncle Henry.

ALLISON Funny you should mention that. There's a second group of hard men in Long Kesh who think that you're spying for the first group.

They stare at each other for a moment and then laugh.

BRIAN   You know, if we get shot, we won't even have the satisfaction of knowing who pulled the trigger.

ALLISON   Don't!

BRIAN   Joke, love.

ALLISON   Sometimes I think it's all a very sick joke and we're destined to die laughing. A great life we'd have together. Drawing the curtains before dark. Jumping every time a car stops outside the house.

BRIAN   We could always emigrate. There must be more Irishmen than kangaroos in Australia by now.

ALLISON   I don't want to live in Australia. I want to live here. I want rain in the summer and snow at Easter. I want grey skies and green grass. I want a baby. I want you.

BRIAN   Then we'll stay and prove them all wrong. We'll open the curtains and the front door. And we'll laugh. Show the world that it's all just a silly Irish joke.

ALLISON   Are you asking me to marry you?

BRIAN   Will you, Allison Clarke, promise to have a baby a year and bring them all up to be good little Catholics, and give them ethnic names like Maraid, Sinea, Fergus and Finbar?

ALLISON   Will you, Brian Rafferty, promise to wear an orange sash on the twelfth of July, and beat a big drum in a kick-the-Pope band?

BRIAN   You know something? When you and me get together, Ulster will never know what hit it. We'll be on the Gloria Hunniford show. Co-founders of the Apathetic Party for people who just don't want to know. We won't have a manifesto.

ALLISON   We'll be too apathetic to write one.

BRIAN   We won't have any members.

ALLISON   They'll be too apathetic to join.

BRIAN   We won't have a cause.

ALLISON	Apathetic people don't have causes.
BRIAN	They tell great jokes though.
ALLISON	I love you.
BRIAN	I know.
ALLISON	My parents are away for the weekend.
BRIAN	Well, what are we doing sitting here, when we could be lying in a big Protestant ascendancy bed up the Malone road?
ALLISON	If we do that, you might have to marry me.
BRIAN	And would you?
ALLISON	I might. If you ask me again in the morning.

Spotlight on the COMEDIAN

COMEDIAN   How do you recognize the bride and groom at an Irish wedding? She's the one in the white wellies. He's the one in the flared wellies.

Did you hear about the girl who wanted to marry an Irishman, but her parents refused to give their consent. So the lovers decided to commit suicide by jumping off the Lagan Bridge. The girl hit the water alright. But the Irishman got lost on the way down.

What do you call an Irishman who marries a gorilla? A social climber.

BRIAN	I love you.
ALLISON	I know.

They exit, arms around each other.

The IRISHMAN *walks on and reads a news bulletin.*

IRISHMAN   The two bodies discovered early this morning near the Cave Hill on the outskirts of Belfast, have been identified as twenty-five year-old Allison Clarke and twenty-nine year-old Brian Rafferty. Miss Clarke was the niece of the Unionist politician Mr Henry Sinclair, who today claimed that the I.R.A. were responsible, and called on the Secretary of State for Northern Ireland to order more troops into the province for the protection of its British citizens. However, a police spokesman said today that Brian Rafferty comes from a family with known Republican sympathies. His brother Joseph is serving a life sentence in the Maze Prison for terrorist offences including bombing and murder. Police say that they are keeping an open mind as to the identity of the killers, and have appealed for information. The bodies were discovered at 6.00 a.m. by an army patrol . . .

COMEDIAN   It was reported in the American newspapers today that there was a Belfast type shooting in Chicago. 'Isn't it funny,' said the Irishman, who was reading the death notices in the Belfast Telegraph, 'how people always seem to die in alphabetical order.'

Did you hear about the Irishman standing in front of the firing squad, who was asked if he'd like a last cigarette? 'No thanks,' he said, 'I'm trying to give them up.'

An Irishman and an Irish girl were pushed off the top of the Cave Hill. Who hit the ground first? Who cares, so long as they're both Irish.

How do you save an Irishman from dying? You don't know? Good.

The IRISHMAN *tears the news bulletin into shreds.*

COMEDIAN   Hallo Paddy. You still here? (*He walks to the* IRISHMAN.) Have you heard the Irish knock knock joke? You haven't? Right, you start.

IRISHMAN   (*expressionlessly*): Knock. Knock.

COMEDIAN   Who's there?

He laughs and begins to walk away.

IRISHMAN   (*quietly*): What do you call an Irishman with a machine gun?

COMEDIAN   I don't know, Paddy. What *do* you call an Irishman with a machine gun?

IRISHMAN   (*wearily*): You call him sir.

Blackout.

QUESTIONS AND EXPLORATIONS

Joyriders

1 Keeping Track

The Prologue

What impact will be made on the audience by the opening song?

Act One

1 What is the significance of the play the characters are watching at the beginning of the act?
2 What initial impressions do we receive of the characters from their responses to the play?
3 How does Arthur behave towards Sandra? How does she respond?
4 What do we learn about Tommy's political views? Who do you think he means when he speaks of knowing 'a few of the lads'?
5 How does Kate speak to the others? What is her relationship to them?
6 What caused Arthur's injuries?
7 What seems to have happened to Maureen's mother?
8 How does the writer show us that the teenagers have never been to the theatre before?
9 What is going on in the stage directions at the start of scene two? How would Tommy act?
10 How would Maureen behave when she speaks about Johnnie?
11 What tone does Tommy use when he speaks to Kate?
12 What is Sandra's attitude to the Youth Training Scheme?
13 As the person in charge of the scheme, what problems does Kate have to cope with?

14 What do we learn about Arthur from the way he talks about his home and about cooking?

15 What are Kate's feelings about love and marriage?

16 How is Tommy affected by his mixed race parentage?

17 How does Arthur hope to win compensation for his injuries?

18 Why does Arthur get angry with Tommy? How does he behave when he talks to Kate?

19 How would the audience react to Maureen's speech at the end of the act?

Act Two

1   Why does Sandra pour scorn on the American Holiday Program?

2   What frustrates Tommy about Sandra? What 'Party' do you think he belongs to?

3   Why does Maureen get so upset?

4   How do the terrorists usually deal with law-breakers like Johnnie and Tommy?

5   How does the incident with the stolen bottle highlight the differences between Arthur and Sandra?

6   Why does Kate dislike the idea of the open day?

7   Who broke Tommy's hands and why?

8   How had the Army responded?

9   How does Sandra react to the knowledge that Maureen is pregnant?

10 What do we learn about Maureen's life from this scene?

11 How do you react to Maureen's thoughts about her future with the baby?

12 Explain the meaning of the signs Sandra makes for the open day.

13 How would Maureen behave as she tries on the new outfit?

14 Why do the police come for Maureen?

15 What explanation does she give for stealing the clothes?

16 How would an actor show Arthur's state of mind when

he hears the gunfire?

17 How was Maureen shot?

18 How does Sandra act when she brings in Maureen's body?

19 Which of the alternative endings to scene three do you think would be the more effective? Why?

20 What does Arthur plan to do with his compensation money? How has he changed since the last scene? What offer does he make to Sandra?

21 What do we learn about Sandra from her monologue?

22 How would the audience feel at the end of the play?

2 Explorations

A Characters

Arthur

1 'They make fun of me round here, ye know. Men don't cook in West Belfast.' How does Arthur deal with other people's criticism and prejudices?

2 'You can be shot to bits and not be dead.' How have Arthur's injuries affected his life?

3 'You're full of big plans that'll come to nuthin' because yer too soft an' yer too easy goin'.' Do you agree with Sandra's assessment of Arthur? Do you think he will make a success of his business?

Sandra

4 'Nobody is never gonna give us nuthin'.' To what extent do the events of the play support Sandra's assertion?

5 'I stole a car once . . . all by myself . . . I never told nobody.' What does this story illustrate about Sandra's character?

6 'This is what it's like. Do you hear me? It's not lovely an' it's not romantic like in stupid friggin' plays!' Do you see Sandra as a cynic or a realist? Explain your views.

7   Do you think Sandra would ever accept Arthur's offer of marriage? Use evidence from the play to support your opinions.

Kate

8   'I'm an incurable optimist. I still have a romantic belief that if an idea is good and right, then it's possible.' What is Kate's attitude to the training scheme, and how does she cope with the many problems of running it?

9   'You know what I am . . . a shadow of a socialist.' 'I might as well live on the moon for all I know.' Can Kate ever really understand the problems which the teenagers on her scheme have to face?

10 Imagine that Kate keeps a diary. Write three or four entries for it, showing her thoughts and feelings at different points in the play. You might wish to include some of the following:
    The theatre trip
    The celebration dinner
    Her relationship with Roger Elliott
    Her attitude to the authorities: local councillors, visiting civil servants and so on.
    Her reactions to what happens to Arthur, Tommy and Maureen.

11 Write a monologue for Kate right at the end of the play. Write what she says about Maureen's death, about what Sandra has just told her, and her thoughts about any of the other recent events.

Maureen

12 'Tell them she done it for love.' Examine Maureen's relationship with her brother, Johnnie, and explain how it eventually leads to her death.

13 'We're gonna live in an old house behind the university
. . . and every day I'll put you in your pram and
wheel you round the Botanic Gardens . . . '
What does this speech illustrate about Maureen's
character? What do you think her life would have
become if she had not been killed?

Tommy

14 'People like him what sit on the political fence live on
while the innocent die.'
'Terrorists only exist because of corrupt governments.'
What do we learn in the play about Tommy's political
views? Do you think he will change as a result of what
happened to him?

General

15 Write an imagined scene between Maureen and
Johnnie on the morning she finds him sick. Use your
knowledge of the characters from the whole play, and
show clearly Maureen's worries about her brother.

16 Imagine and write two conversations between Arthur
and his father. The first should be before the court's
judgement, and the second after Arthur has been
awarded the compensation. Show what you know of
their characters from your study of the play.

17 Write the report on Maureen's death, and the
circumstances that led to it, which might appear in the
local newspaper.

18 Choose one of the following characters: Kate, Sandra,
Arthur, Tommy. Write a monologue for your character
six months after the end of the play. Describe what has
become of them, and of any of the others. Try to
capture the way the character would speak, and convey
their attitudes and feelings as convincingly as you can.

B Themes

1   *Joyriders* is set very specifically in Belfast. How
    important is that setting to the action of the play? Make
    detailed reference to the text in your answer.

2   'Do you know what this scheme is? It's a friggin'
    government joyride. A good laugh for a year, an' then
    you grow up.' From all the comments and evidence in
    the play, what is your assessment of the YTS scheme? Are
    there any ways in which it might be improved, or are
    there so many problems that it is just a waste of time?

3   What evidence, from the songs, and from elsewhere in
    the play, does the writer give us of life in the Divis
    Flats? How do these compare with the house and
    district where Kate lives?

4   In what ways is the play's title appropriate?

5   The play's message can be seen to be relentlessly bleak.
    Do you find anything here to be optimistic about?

C In Performance

1   Design and sketch a set which would be simple and
    adaptable enough to work for the whole play. Add
    explanatory notes to describe the props you would use,
    and the changes you would make to indicate the
    theatre, the workshop, Kate's house and the art gallery.

2   Choose any one of the characters and write instructions
    to the actor who is to play the role. Explain the
    qualities of character they will need to portray, and
    suggest how they might use gestures, actions, facial
    expressions and tone of voice to convey these qualities
    to an audience.

3   In the scene where Maureen is shot, most of the action
    occurs off-stage. How, as a director, would you hope to
    convey the tension and drama of this scene? Give
    details about the actors' movements and expressions,
    and about any sound effects or lighting changes.

4   Choose two or three of the play's songs and describe in

detail how you think they should be performed.
Who sings them? What actions or movements take
place during the songs? Would there be lighting
changes? What accompaniment, if any, would you
want?

3 Criticism

1 'The action accelerates to a hideously plausible climax
from which it appears that the machine-gunned
Maureen and the 'illegible bachelor' Arthur are not cut
out for survival in Belfast; and that nothing will be
solved by those who find some comfortable berth away
from the firing line.' (Irving Wardle, *The Times*)
To what extent do you agree with this critic's
interpretation of the ending of the play?
2 'Although Reid has a fine gift for creating character,
here she seems at a loss to find a convincing context for
them.' (Suzie MacKenzie, *Time Out*)
How do you respond to this criticism of the plot of
Joyriders?
3 'What makes *Joyriders* so impressive is the way that it
suggests the extent to which a new generation has
grown up without hope and has adjusted with grace
and jauntiness to lives bounded by pessimism.'
(Nicholas de Jongh, *The Guardian*)
What evidence do you find in the play of the qualities
to which this critic refers?

Did You Hear The One About the Irishman . . .?

1 Keeping Track

1 What is your response to hearing the lists of permitted
Christmas parcels alongside the comedian's jokes?

2   What relevance do the lists have for Brian and Marie?
3   Why do you think Allison asks Brian to call back when her mother comes into the room?
4   Why does Allison dislike Susan?
5   What relation is Susan to Brian?
6   Why does Mrs Clarke not approve of Allison's relationship with Brian?
7   What routines do visitors have to go through when they visit relatives in the Maze?
8   What are Marie's feelings about Protestants?
9   What happened to Brian and Marie's father, and to their mother?
10 Who is Allison's Uncle Henry and why do his opinions matter?
11 Why does Mr Clarke tell Allison the story about his early days of running the factory?
12 How does Allison react to her father's warnings?
13 Why is Bernie Cassidy not pleased that her husband has been released from jail?
14 Can you think of any explanations for the rules about clothing allowed for remand prisoners?
15 Why is Marie cool with her Aunt, Mrs Boyd?
16 Why does Brian insist on checking in Hughie's parcel?
17 Why did Mrs Boyd's parents refuse to go to her sister's wedding?
18 What was unusual about the relationship between Paddy Rafferty and Sammy Boyd?
19 What motive could terrorists have had for shooting Paddy Rafferty?
20 Why did a woman spit in Isa Boyd's face at her brother-in-law's funeral?
21 How did Joe and Hughie come to be enemies?
22 Why is Mrs Boyd worried about Brian?
23 What warning does Hughie give to Allison?
24 What does Joe warn Brian about?

25 What do you learn about Brian's views from his speech about the children he teaches? How would his manner change during this speech?

26 What amuses Allison and Brian about the threats that have been issued against them?

27 Why do they not wish to emigrate? What other options are open to them?

28 How would the audience react to the news report of Brian and Allison's murders?

29 How does the tone of the jokes change at the end of the play?

2 Explorations

A Characters

Brian

1 'Outside of here, in the real world, fellas and girls still go out together. To the pubs, the parks, the pictures. Normal life goes on, Joe, outside those wire fences.' What actions does Brian take to pursue what he describes as 'normal life' in spite of the problems he faces?

2 'Are you ever serious about anything?' What things does Brian take seriously? Find evidence in the text to support your answer.

3 Brian: It's never too late to hold out your hand.
Marie: You're a dreamer. They'd tie your hands behind your back and shoot you.
Look closely at Brian's relationship with his sister, Marie. Can you account for their very different attitudes?

4 Look back at Brian's speech about the children he teaches. ('One of the kids came up to me in school yesterday . . . the men with the most guns win.') What do we learn here about Brian's feelings about The Troubles and the incidents that have shaped his attitudes?

Allison

5   'If I thought for one moment that me marrying a
    Catholic would put a stop to Uncle Henry's career, as
    you call it, I'd marry the first Catholic who'd have me.'
    'Bigoted opinions don't bother me.' Examine Allison's
    attitude to the threats and warnings she receives from
    fellow Protestants, and to sectarian attitudes in general.
    Find evidence in the text to support your ideas.

6   Look again at the conversations Allison has with both
    her parents. How far is she influenced by them?

7   'Can't you be serious about anything?' What does
    Allison take seriously? Compare this statement (made
    by Mrs Clarke) with what Marie says to Brian. (See
    question 2)

Mr Clarke

8   'I was naive enough to believe that good intentions can
    save the world. Your Brian is like that.' What does Mr
    Clarke think of Allison's relationship with Brian?

9   'What is happening now in this country has come about
    not just because of greedy politicians, but because of
    people like me. Influential people of my generation who
    knew it was wrong, but did nothing to change it.' How
    responsible do you think Mr Clark and people like him
    are for the continuing hostilities in Northern Ireland?
    What could he have done to change things?

Mrs Boyd

10 What is Mrs Boyd's family background, and what has
    it taught her?

Marie

11 How has Marie been affected by what happened to her
    parents? How does this influence her attitude to Brian's
    relationship with Allison?

General

12 Draw up a family tree to map the relationships between the characters in the play. Indicate which community each of them belongs to, Protestant or Catholic.

13 'Where else in Northern Ireland can a Provie wife and a UDA wife take a long look at each other and realise that they're both on board the same sinking ship? Common ground. Common enemy. And there's nothing like a common enemy for resolving a family feud.' Imagine and write a scene set in the visitors' area of the Maze Prison after the deaths of Allison and Brian. Include some or all of the following characters: Mrs Boyd, Marie Rafferty, Bernie Cassidy, and show how you think they would be affected by the deaths.

14 Write a scene that takes place in the Clarke household after the deaths of Allison and Brian. Show clearly the characters of Mr and Mrs Clarke using your knowledge of them from the play. You may include Henry Sinclair (Allison's politician uncle) if you wish. Use stage directions to indicate how the characters should act.

B Themes

1 'Sometimes I think it's a very sick joke.' Make a study of how different types of humour are used in the play.

2 Do you think that Allison and Brian were wrong to continue seeing each other after their lives were threatened? Should they have settled for a quiet life apart?

3 What do we learn from the play about conditions in The Maze Prison? To what extent does the jail reflect the situation in Northern Ireland as a whole?

C In Performance

1 In a past production of the play, the roles of Joe Rafferty and Hughie Boyd were played by the same actor. What dramatic possibilities are suggested to you by this doubling up? If you were to mount your own production of the play, also using one actor for both parts, how would you make use of costume, props, set design and the actor's own performance to bring out the similarities or differences between these two characters?

2   Look at the parts of the Irishman and the comedian, who stand outside the main action of the play. As a director, what advice would you give to the actors playing these roles? Think about their relative positions on stage; timing and tone of voice in the delivery of the lines; whether their 'characters' develop during the play. Add notes about how you might use lighting, set design and props to enhance their roles.

3 Criticism

1   '*Did You Hear the One About the Irishman . . . ?* is an exploration of prejudice where no one is immune and where the jokes are no joke.' (Peggy Butcher, *Time Out*) Collect and comment on the examples of prejudice to be found in the play.

2   'When I write a play I don't set out to make political points – I always start by writing about characters I know.' (Christina Reid) What political points has Reid, nevertheless, made in this play?

3   'There tend to be more women in my plays because I have spent more time during my life with women than with men . . . I always find the women much stronger and more decisive than men, so they tend to emerge more clearly.' (Christina Reid) Compare the male and female characters in the play. Do you agree that the women emerge more clearly?

GLOSSARY

Joyriders

49	*wise up*	stop fooling yourself
49	*wired to the moon*	crazy
49	*DSO*	dick shot off (also Distinguished Service Order)
51	*hivin'*	swarming
57	*Stormont Castle*	a government building
59	*suspect device*	a possible bomb
61	*coked to the gills*	drugged (probably from glue)
63	*bedlam*	a mad house
68	*takin' a hand out him*	making fun of him
69	*klute*	left-handed

Did You Hear the One About the Irishman . . . ?

Page

73	*The Maze Prison*	also known as Long Kesh, a prison where terrorists are held
73	*H blocks*	cell blocks, so called because of their shape
74	*Compound 17*	section of Long Kesh – a cell block
80	*Prods*	Protestants
80	*Fenians*	Catholics
81	*on the blanket*	a refusal to wear prison uniform as a protest at being denied political status
81	*Provie*	member of Provisional IRA
81	*UDA*	Ulster Defence Association (a Protestant terrorist organisation)
86	*internment*	imprisonment
87	*black beret and dark glasses*	'uniform' worn by IRA terrorists
87	*remand prisoner*	someone who is awaiting trial
88	*Vat 69*	a brand of whisky
90	*the troubles*	violence committed for political reasons
90	*sectarian*	committed against someone of an opposing religion
92	*Ian Paisley*	leader of the Democratic Unionist Party in Northern Ireland
94	*penance*	a punishment for sin
94	*Hail Marys*	short prayers